To [...]
H[...] [...]y
whatever!
Geoff & Sarah

OWLS

A Guide for Ornithologists

Barn Owls *(Tyto alba)*

OWLS

A Guide for Ornithologists

Carole Pugh

RON FREETHY

Photographs
by
Eric and David Hosking
(unless otherwise stated)

The author dedicates this book to the memory of Eric Hosking with thanks for his friendship and help.

All enquiries and requests, relevant to this title should be sent to the publisher, Bishopsgate Press Ltd, 15 Tonbridge Road, Hildenborough, Kent.

Printed in Hong Kong through GlobalCom

Contents

Acknowledgments

No book on such a fascinating and complex order of birds as owls could be produced in isolation. I am grateful to artists Carole Pugh and Ian Lambert and to Michael Edwards for the use of one of his photographs.

Although the whole book is dedicated to Eric Hosking I must express my gratitude to Eric and his son David who I have counted among my friends for many years. Eric was always generous with his time and ever modest about his photographic skills. These traits live on in David.

I am grateful to Brian Oldfield for his observations on the diet of owls in Lancashire, to Peter Steyn's work on the owls of South Africa and to Jeff Watson who wrote so well about the Seychelles owl.

Finally I thank my wife Marlene who typed the manuscript and checked the proofs, taking time out from her own publications to look for my errors.

RON FREETHY
MARCH 1992

Cover photograph *Tawny Owl* photographed by Brian Oldfield

PREFACE

In 1972 I sat in a hide overlooking the grey February sea off Walney Island in south Cumbria. My self-appointed task was to study the increasing flock of Eider Ducks, a project then in its twentieth year. As the tide receded I put down my pencil and notebook, poured myself a coffee from my flask and blew on my chilled hands. Soon the mud flats were exposed; flocks of waders began to arrive to get down to the serious business of feeding before the onset of a freezing cold night. Suddenly a flock of almost a thousand Dunlins lifted from the shore and whirled into the air — all except one reached the safety of the sky. The slowest Dunlin to rise was struck down by a bird of prey which dragged it to the shelter of a washed-up oil drum and began to eat it.

Expecting to focus on a Merlin, I brought up my binoculars only to find that the predator was a Little Owl. Later, in the warmth of an armchair in front of a driftwood fire, and by the light of an oil lamp, I read all I could about the Little Owl, and I have been fascinated by all owls ever since. My bookshelves groaned under the weight of owl books, my study table became littered with pellets, and files bulged with field notes and magazine articles culled from all over the world.

In order to conserve birds of prey one needs competent professional ornithologists and learned books full of statistics on wing measurements, feet and leg lengths and egg measurements. We have these. We also need fieldwork by fascinated amateurs and books which summarise what we know — and, more important, what we do not know. This book is written for that second group in the hope that it will set someone off 'owling throughout the world'. If one more species is documented because of interest sparked off by this book then it will have served its purpose.

Note: Throughout this work I describe owl noises as 'woo', 'hu' and 'keevit', etc., but it has to be admitted that describing bird calls in human language is all but impossible. The modern method of describing bird sounds is to record them, play the recording through a special machine called a *sonograph* and then photograph the sound waves. Such a photograph is called a *sonogram*.

CHAPTER ONE

What is an Owl?

Owls are often described as cats with wings, which, in non-scientific terms, is a reasonable thing to say. Being birds, however, their bodies are constructed on an entirely different plan from that of any mammal. We should first consider the anatomy of birds in general and then of owls in particular.

Birds and flight

With regard to its flight efficiency, the two most essential features of a bird's body are its feathers and its light skeleton. In order to develop wings to be used specifically for flight, birds have had to sacrifice the more generalised use of their front limbs. This has meant that they have become bipedal. The bones themselves are invariably light, hollow and therefore less weighty than those of a mammal. This must mean some loss of strength, although there has been compensation for this through the formation of internal struts which separate the air-filled spaces. (It is no accident that aircraft designers have developed a similar design.) The hollow bones are often connected to the lungs and air sacs, thus providing an extra air supply when required.

The Wing and Skeleton

A look at the arm and hand of a human will reveal many features also present in the wing of a bird. There are enough similarities between the two to prove that both developed from a common reptilian ancestor. We have five fingers, but in the bird's wing these have been reduced to three and only the second of them is at all well developed. The thumb has lost the power of independent movement and is usually referred to as the 'bastard wing', although scientists call it the alula. This loss of mobility has been sacrificed for a reason; the alula is held at the correct angle to maintain a smooth flow of air over the wing — an essential feature if stalling is to be prevented.

The flight feathers are described as either primary or secondary. Primary feathers are carried on the manus area of the wing — an area including the carpometacarpus (wrist area) and digitial phalanges; secondary feathers are carried on the bird's equivalent of a human's forearm (ulna bone).

The primary feathers are driven through the air by powerful flight muscles attached to the keel; should these be damaged, flight becomes impossible. The secondaries are essential for providing lift, and experiments on captive birds have shown that a bird is still able to fly with only half of these feathers working, although it is not as manoeuverable as usual. Each feather is able to function independently and the shape of the wing can therefore be altered easily during flight — even our most sophisticated aircraft design cannot achieve this degree of efficiency.

In the case of owls, the secondary feathers are particulary important because the birds feeding success depends upon their flight efficiency; also vital are the tail feathers (retrices), which function as a braking system.

We should, at this point, also say something about the so-called 'silent flight' of owls. In a normal feather there is a system of 'hooks and eyes', or barbs, which interlock to create a hard surface which beats the air like a fan, and actually sounds like one too. The leading edge of owls' primary feathers do not have this interlocking system, and thus a soft sound-muffling fringe is created. The trailing edge of the wing is also softened in a like fashion. This sound insulation is not without a disadvantage, however; it causes much more drag during flight and thus places more reliance on the efficiency of the secondary feathers.

In addition to flight feathers, birds also have contour feathers and down feathers which, respectively, provide body shape and insulation. In owls these feathers are again softer and perhaps bulkier and more numerous, as anyone who has ever handled an owl will readily verify. More than 10,000 down feathers have been counted on a Long-eared Owl.

Owl flight also depends upon a factor known as wing loading.

$$\textbf{wing loading} \quad = \quad \frac{\text{wing area (in cm}^2)}{\text{weight (in gm)}}$$

This calculation establishes the area of the wing divided by the body weight which it has to support. A bird with a high wing loading, such as an owl, is more agile in the air and can fly more slowly than one with a low loading, such as a swan. Thus it is obviously easier for an owl to seek food while in the air.

Feathers are obviously essential to flight, but equally essential are the powerful muscles which provide the power. The humerus bone of the upper arm is short, flat and broad, thus providing a spacious anchorage for the pectoral muscle. The other anchorage is provided by the breast bone, otherwise known as the sternum, and above this are the coracoid bones which resist the inevitable compression during flight. Thus we have a rigid thorax comprising a ring of bones — scapulas, corocoids and clavicles (collar bones), the latter being fused together to form the furcula (wishbone). There is also a great deal of fusion of vertebrae, ribs and hip girdle, all perfectly designed to resist compression and assist the wings in providing thrust.

Compared to a mammal the ribs of a bird consist mainly of bone and not of cartilage. They form solid joints with the thoracic vertebrae, all save one of which are fused together. Each rib has what is called an uncinate process — a sort of strut which slopes backwards to join the rib immediately behind it. The sternal ribs join both the sternum and the vertebral ribs. Here, once more, we find a solid protective box.

Yet another U-shaped box is formed by a thin, but strong, plate-like structure called the synsacrum, which is made up of thirteen vertebrae fused to the pelvic girdle. This protects the gut and body organs. Anchorage for both the tail feathers and body muscles is provided by the pygostyle — often called the 'parson's nose'. This is also composed of fused vertebrae, but this time only four bones are joined together. The synsacrum and the pygostyle are separated by six unfused caudal vertebrae.

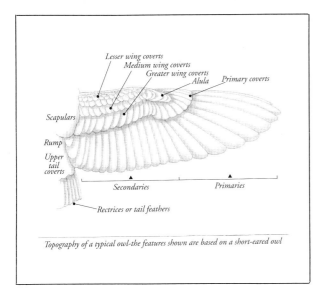

Lesser wing coverts
Medium wing coverts
Greater wing coverts
Alula
Primary coverts
Scapulars
Rump
Upper tail coverts
Secondaries
Primaries
Rectrices or tail feathers

Topography of a typical owl-the features shown are based on a short-eared owl

Topography of a typical owl — the features shown are based on a short-eared owl. Artist Ian Lambert

The body organs

Any living organism that is as active as a bird requires particularly efficient respiratory, circulatory and digestive systems. There is often confusion between respiration and breathing. Respiration is a chemical process whereby energy is released from food, and is represented by the chemical formula:

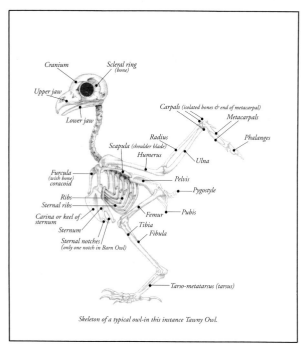

Skeleton of a typical owl — in this instance Tawny Owl. Artist Ian Lambert

$$C_6H_{12}O_6 + 6O_2 \longrightarrow 6CO_2 + 6H_2O + energy$$

Glucose + Oxygen ⟵ Carbon + water + energy
Sugar   Dioxide

Breathing is the method whereby respiratory gases are brought into (oxygen) and pushed out (carbon dioxide) of the body. This process is purely physical and the word 'breathing' is now very sensibly being replaced by 'ventilation'. Because we humans are mammals, we tend to assume that the possession of a pair of lungs which function like bellows, pumped by a muscle called the diaphragm, is the only suitable method of ventilation. The bird, however, requires more energy in flight than can ever be demanded by a land-based mammal (although bats have had to overcome similar problems). Bats, however, do not fly at such high altitudes, nor do they sustain flight for as long as birds.

Movement of the wings and flight muscles draws air into the body where it passes straight through the lungs and fills the air sacs and the hollow bones. The bird thus carries its own 'built-in' air tanks. Oxygen can only be absorbed into the blood stream via the lungs, however,

and the stored gases wait to be drawn upon as required. Carbon dioxide passes back into the lungs from the blood and, compared to mammals, very little residual air remains here after exhalation.

Much as we mammals may feel 'out-done', the bird's ventilation system is more efficient than ours. An active bird's muscles must generate a great deal of heat and it is thought that excess heat may be passed out of the body via the air sacs. This is essential because the feathers of a bird cover the skin and prevent any loss of heat via this organ.

Having a smooth exchange of respiratory gases is one thing, but the provision of an efficient heart and circulatory system is quite another. This system must be under great strain to deliver oxygen and food to areas of high metabolic activity, such as working muscles, and the removal of carbon dioxide and other waste products from these areas is equally vital.

The bird's heart is a large, powerful organ undergoing rapid muscular contractions. In both birds and mammals it is generally true to say that the smaller a species is, the larger will be its relative heart size compared to body weight, and the quicker will be its heart rate. It is also generally true that, gram for gram of body weight, birds have larger and faster hearts than mammals. In a human the heart weight is 0.42 per cent of body weight with an average resting pulse rate of 72. In the House Sparrow these figures are 1.68 per cent of body weight with a resting pulse rate of 460. In the Tawny Owl the figures are 1.30 per cent, with a pulse rate of around 300.

As one would expect, the body temperature of a bird is around 42°C, some 5°C above that of a human adult. To maintain these high-powered systems birds require large quantities of food — it has been estimated that a Barn Owl may require a daily intake of around 20 per cent of its body weight. Because they are so well insulated owls may require rather less food than other birds of a similar size. Digestion must also be very rapid, and the whole process takes less than six hours. Owls invariably swallow their prey whole; indigestible material such as bones, teeth, fur, beaks or insect exoskeletons are compressed into a pellet and egested through the mouth. Contrary to what many people believe, pellet production is not confined to birds of prey — indeed, more than 350 species have been found to produce pellets. It may well be that most species produce pellets, although perhaps not as regularly as

Pygmy Owl *(Glaucidium brasilianum)*

owls. Many naturalists enjoy collecting owl pellets which are then teased apart and their contents identified. Mammals can be identified from skulls, jaws and teeth, and birds from beaks, feet, bones and feathers. Some experts are even able to identify several species of earthworm from the shape of the setae (or bristles) which are found on each of their body segments and with the help of which they move.

The pellets of some owl species are more easily collected than others — those of the Barn Owl are particularly predictable as they expel the pellets at their regular roost. Tawny Owls, in contrast, egest pellets at any one of several feeding and roosting sites and may spread their pellets throughout their home woodland. In temperate regions of the world, where they have been studied more closely than in other regions, owls produce one or two pellets during a 24-hour cycle, but this depends to some degree on the season. In summer, when the nights are short, only one pellet is produced beneath the daytime roost. This is usually large. In winter, when they have a longer time in which to hunt, they produce one large pellet followed by a second smaller pellet about seven or eight hours later. Contrary to what is often stated the ejection of pellets is a conscious act, and not a reflex action.

How and where is the pellet actually formed? Although the physiology and mechanism of pellet formation have been examined using radioactive tracers, there is a great deal left to discover. The undigested material, which has been separated in the gizzard, is apparently held in the proventriculus (an enlargement of the stomach) by a mechanical barrier. Disgorging a pellet via the specially thickened oesophagus can be easy, but a bird sometimes experiences difficulty and the process may take up to an hour, the individual concerned looking very uncomfortable indeed.

Owl senses

In order to obtain adequate supplies of food, birds, especially predatory species, require efficient eyes and ears. Owls have often been very accurately described as general predators with respect to the food they eat. They are, however, perfectly adapted for hunting at night, a niche occupied by less than 3 per cent of all

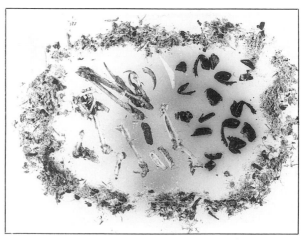

A dissected owl pellet showing the remains of beetles, birds and mammals.

birds, of which percentage around half are owls. For many years their efficiency was attributed to their excellent night vision, but this has proved to be an oversimplification because no eye is capable of functioning if the cells in the retina are not stimulated and, clearly, stimulation is impossible in total darkness. As many owls are able to catch food in total darkness, however, we must look for another method of receiving stimuli — and in this hearing plays an essential role. Thus the eyes and ears of owls should be given equal credit for their hunting success.

To house such important organs it is not surprising to find that owls have huge skulls with prominent eyes and ear holes (owls do not have earlobes like mammals). A look at a diagram will show the basic differences between the mammalian and avian eye. The owl's eye is shaped more like a tube than a sphere and this means that it has a much reduced field of view — around 110° compared to our 180° — but owls have solved this. Humorists have suggested that if you walk slowly around a roosting owl it will follow your progress and eventually wring its own neck! What the frontally placed eyes do provide is a degree of binocular vision which enables a hunting owl to judge distances when pouncing on its prey.

There are other myths about owls' vision which must also be dispelled. Do owls' eyes only function in bad light and become useless as the light intensity increases? The answer to both of these questions is no. On average, their 'night vision' is only two or three times more efficient that ours and some workers feel that a human being with good night sight may well be as efficient as a below-average owl. Neither have the researchers found that bright light 'overloads' the owl retina. Furthermore, it is known that some owls, including the Tawny, have a degree of colour vision.

How do we know these things? Light is focused by the lens onto the retina of the eye. This tissue is made up of two main types of cell, rods and cones. Rods respond to light intensity and cones respond to colour. Thus, by counting the numbers of these cells it is possible to get an accurate impression of the efficiency of the eye of a species and also to compare the relative performance of individuals.

At one time it was suggested that the Little Owl could respond to infra-red radiation produced by warm-blooded animals, but this theory has now been discounted. What is quite clear, even from the above brief account, is that an owl which relied entirely on its eyesight for finding food would soon starve to death. Let us therefore consider its sense of hearing.

The ear is thought to have first evolved in fish as an organ of balance and this is still one of its main functions. The positioning of the ears relative to the eyes is similar in both birds and mammals, but birds lack the pinna (external earlobe) and a straight tube carries the sound waves to the ear drum, causing it to

vibrate. The middle section of the ear consists of an air-filled cavity which functions like the sound box of a musical instrument. Roughly equivalent to the instrument's string is a long slender bone called the columella, which serves to amplify the sound. In mammals the columella is replaced by three bones — the hammer, anvil and stirrup, so named because of their shape.

The inner ear of a bird also exhibits differences when compared to that found in mammals. There is a complex system of labyrinths, fluid-filled canals, which are themselves suspended in a bath of fluid. There are five sections in the system, the utricle and semi-circular canals being concerned with balance. The sacculus, cochlea and lagena are concerned with the transmission of, and further amplification of, sound. The cochlea transforms sound waves into nerve impulses which are then transmitted along the auditory nerve to the brain which can then filter, interpret and react to the sound. The lagena contains tiny granules of calcium carbonate, called earstones or otoliths. This area is thought to deal with the reception of low-frequency sounds, leaving the high frequencies to be dealt with by the sacculus and cochlea. The efficiency of an owl's ear can be seen by reference to the frequency range of various species

Species	Lower limit	Maximum sensitivity	Upper limit
Mallard	300	2500	8000
Long-eared Owl	100	6000	18000
Starling	100	2000	15000
Chaffinch	200	3200	29000

(units quoted are given in Hertz [cycles per second]

The important figure is that of maximum sensitivity and it is obvious that owls are particularly sensitive to high-frequency sounds such as the rustling of leaves and the squeaking of small rodents.

The efficiency of the inner ear is one thing, but the correct focusing of sound waves onto the ear drum is another, equally vital requirement. The prominent facial disc possessed by very many species functions like a sophisticated ear trumpet and the rim is provided with stiffened feathers which reflect sound in much the same way as the long mobile external ears (pinnae) of hares

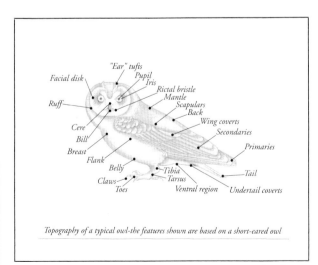

Topography of a typical owl-the features shown are based on a short-eared owl

Topography of a typical owl — the features shown are based on a short-eared owl. Artist Ian Lambert

and rabbits. The openings to the ears are huge when compared to those mammals and in some species they can run almost the whole length of the skull. They are usually protected by a flap of skin which can be used to alter the length of ear drum exposed. The skull of an owl is very broad, and thus the two ears are widely separated, which means that sound waves will reach one ear fractionally before the other. This enables owls to develop a sort of three-dimensional auditory picture, a vital clue when locating prey. In some of the particularly nocturnal species the two ear openings are sited at different levels, a further aid to the reception of 'three-dimensional sound'.

Bills and talons

From the above account we can see how good owls are at locating their prey, but how do they kill it? It is not the bill which does their killing, but the immensely powerful claws. The bill looks more dangerous than it actually is because during evolution it had to be deflected downwards in order not to interfere with the line of vision from the huge eyes. In any case, owls do not need very powerful bills to tear up their food, as do many diurnal birds of prey, because owls swallow their prey whole. The strength of the owl is in its legs, feet and phenomenally sharp claws. The outer toe is also reversible, which means that it can be used forwards or backwards, and thus the owl's 'gripping area' is greatly increased. The legs are feathered down to the toes, for which feature there are two explanations: it could be to conserve heat or to counteract the bite of any small mammal, obviously reluctant to be killed. In my view the feathered legs serve both of these functions.

Some species, such as the Fish Owls, lack feathered legs, which would obviously hinder their ability to hunt in water. Instead of feathers these species have naked legs and they also have spines on the soles of their feet to improve their hold on the slippery fish.

A pair of young tawny owls waiting to be fed.

Great Horned Owl   *(Bubo virginianus)*

Barn Owl   *(Tyto alba)*   *drawing by Carole Pugh.*

CHAPTER TWO

The Evolution and Classification of Owls

More than 8,600 species of birds exist at the present time and they are divided into 27 orders, of which the owls make up one — the Strigiformes which, as we have seen, fill the niche of nocturnal predators. The order is sub-divided into two families — the Tytonidae (Barn, Grass and Bay Owls) and the Strigidae (often called typical owls). Before going into the details of how these families are classified, we need to consider how they evolved and here we find two competing theories. Did they arise from one common ancestor or from two? The only possible way of resolving this question is to look for possible ancestors. What is certain is that the ancestor or ancestors are now extinct and we must search them out in the murky and complex area of fossil birds.

The chances of finding bird fossils are much less than for mammals because the bones of the latter are solid and will not therefore be crushed by sediment deposited on top of them. The hollow bones of birds are obviously much more easily shattered. Aquatic animals, whether bird or mammal, are much more likely to be fossilised since the sedimentary rocks which are ideal for bone preservation are laid down in and around areas of shallow water. Birds such as owls, which are seldom found in these areas, will therefore be less likely to become fossilised and their evolutionary history will thus be more difficult to unravel.

Despite the scarcity of fossil evidence, however, sufficient material is available to build up some sort of history of extinct owls. It seems that they were already distinct as an order between 65 and 90 million years ago — a period known to geologists as the Cretaceous. More than 50 species have so far been investigated, with more than half having features which make them recognisable as Strigidae owls. The great majority of these have been dated to a period earlier than 40 million years (the Upper Eocene period). The fossils which can be grouped into the Tytonidae family seem to be younger and set in the Lower Miocene period, which began around 25 million years ago.

Have we any evidence of owls prior to these obviously Strigidae and Tytonidae owls? Yes we do, but before going on to describe them it should be admitted that the descriptions are often based on only a few bones. North American fossils, discovered in Wyoming, have been dated to the Eocene, tentatively dated at 50 million years and placed in a separate family called the Protostrigidae, literally meaning the 'first owls'. Experts in this difficult field seem certain that the Protostrigidae were nocturnal or crepuscular (active at dawn and dusk) and had a functional facial disc.

Recent discoveries have pushed back owl evolution into the Cretaceous period around 100 million years ago, when the last of the dinosaurs were still holding on. Three species of owl have been described on the basis of a small number of leg bones, mainly the tarso-metatarsi (lower leg). Two species from Romania have been tentatively placed in a fourth owl family named the Bradyenemidae, and taxonomists have fallen into the trap of overdramatising their discoveries by naming one bird *Bradyeneme draculae*. To complete the ancient record, we have an American fossil from Colorado, also identified on the basis of leg bones and dated to the Palaeocene period, which began 65 million years ago.

Let us now see how far back we can trace some of the

Long-eared Owl *(Asio otus) returning to nest to incubate eggs*

species we know today. The main thrust of evolution seems to have taken place between 12 and 25 million years ago (the Miocene period). The present evidence seems to suggest that the Long-eared Owl is the oldest species still alive today, having been dated to the Oligocene period around 36 million years ago. Not only does this place the Long-eared Owl as the oldest owl, but it also makes it one of the longest established of all the 8,600-plus species of birds alive today. In the period between ten and three million years ago — termed the Pleistocene — fossil evidence has shown that almost 40 of the present 146 species of owl were already in existence. Because of the scarcity of fossils, the true percentage is probably much higher than this. A comparison with mammal fossils suggests that owl evolution was a little in advance of the rodents which make up the bulk of their diet at the present time. It is obviously impossible to be certain but it is likely that they fed either upon reptiles, from which both birds and mammals evolved, or long-extinct mammals, but it is probable that both of these types of creature formed a part of the diet of the ancient owls.

Having pointed out that owls form one of the 27 orders of birds, we now come to the question of where to place owls within this classification and what relationship, if any, they have to the other orders. At first all the predatory birds were placed together, but this has since been shown to be far too simplistic. These days it is thought that the diurnal birds of prey (Falconiformes) and the owls had completely different ancestors. This has been proved by an analysis of the proteins found in the white of the eggs of both types of bird. This provides the key to the genetics of each species and we now know that owls are more closely related to nightjars and cuckoos than to the diurnal birds of prey which are more 'primitive' than owls. The fact that both owls and raptors have hooked bills, strong feet and sharp talons is a result of what is called convergent evolution, where body structures gradually develop as a result of interaction between bird and environment. Convergent evolution accounts for the fact that all owls look alike, while their differences can be explained by the term 'adaptive radiation'. By this we mean that owls will evolve variations according to the environment in which they live.

A second term, known as the 'ecological niche', also throws some light on owl classification. This points out that no two similar species are able to survive in the same habitat, feeding upon the same source of food. This can be understood by reference to the five common species of owl resident in Britain, but the same exercise can be extended to the owls of any other part of the world. In Britain the Tawny Owl prefers to inhabit deciduous woodlands and parks, in contrast to the Long-eared Owl which shows a distinct preference for conifers. The Barn Owl may have originally chosen to breed and roost in caves, but has learned, as its name implies, to specialise in feeding upon the rats and mice which are such a pest around farms. The Little Owl frequents hedgerows and stone walls which are not at all suitable for the larger owls. The only British habitat not claimed by the species so far described is open moorland and sand dunes and these areas are claimed by the Short-eared Owl.

When it comes down to the precise classification of owls (see table 2), we should be aware that taxonomy is always in some state of flux. One new species of owl seems to be discovered every ten years or so, while others face the danger of becoming extinct. On this basis we can say that the Tytonidae owls are composed of between ten and twelve species, depending upon the authority consulted, and are arranged in two genera. Members of the family are found throughout Europe, except in the extreme north where they seem unable to

handle the very low temperatures. South East Asia, Africa and South and North America, as far as the Canadian border, also have Tytonidae and they also occur in Australasia. Thus they are among the most cosmopolitan of all owls. They show a preference for open areas, including farmland, where they often have a significant and beneficial effect upon the control of rodents. They are also found in woodland areas, but almost always where the trees are widely spaced in thick grass, or perhaps in the marshy areas between areas of woodland.

Making up the family Strigidae are 134 species, arrranged into 22 genera. They are spread over almost all the globe, except Antarctica. Their habitats include dense forest, woodland, tundra, grassland and even desert.

Owls have fascinated two groups of naturalists which I call natural historians and natural scientists. The former are not just interested in the identification and behaviour of a species, but also in its folklore. The latter concentrate upon scientific accounts of different species, which are sketchy for some birds and must be improved if the species under threat are to be protected and, in a few cases, saved from extinction.

Classification

In order for the study of any species to be thorough we must be sure that all workers are actually describing the same species. To illustrate this point let us consider the Tawny Owl. In France it is known as *Choette Hulotte;* in Germany it is the *Waldkauz;* in Spain *Carabo.* Thank goodness potential chaos has been averted by the sensible practice of alloting each living organism its own unique scientific name.

This was first used by Karl von Linne (1707-78) who is better known by the Latinized form of his name, Linnaeus. In 1735 he published his *Systema Naturae*, which, by the time it reached its tenth edition in 1758, had been streamlined into the system of classification which is still in use today. Although he spent most of his life working as a botanist at the University of Uppsala in his native Sweden, Linnaeus is rightly renowned through-

Tawny Owl

photograph by Michael Edwards

out the world as the father of taxonomy. The secret of his binomial system is its simplicity. Let us see how it helps to solve the problem facing workers from many countries when decribing the species which, in English, is called the Tawny Owl.

Each species is given two names and this combination is unique to that particular organism. The first name, which must begin with a capital letter, indicates the genus. Thus, for the Tawny Owl we have *Strix*. The second name, which starts with a small letter, indicates the species and so we now have *Strix aluco*. By convention in scientific literature, all scientific names are printed in italics and follow the vernacular name. So, in English we have the Tawny Owl (*Strix aluco*). Thus there is no chance of confusion arising during translation — everyone throughout the world will now know which bird is under consideration.

Moving up the scale, several genera are grouped into a family, and by convention the family name of animals ends in 'idae'. Thus the Tawny Owl is a member, as we have seen, of the Strigidae family. The Strigidae are further divided into two sub-families — the Buboninae and the Striginae. Above the family level we have the order and, again by convention, the order ends on the letters 'iformes'. Owls are grouped into the Strigiformes. Above the order we have the categories class, sub-phylum and phylum and the complete classification of the tawny owl is therefore:

Phylum:	Chordata (animals with internal skeltons)
Sub-phylum:	Vertebrata (animals with a bony vertebral column)
Class:	Aves (birds)
Order:	Strigiformes
Family:	Strigidae
Sub-family:	Striginae
Genus:	*Strix*
Species:	*Strix aluco*

The above classification would have satisfied Linnaeus who invented the binomial system, but it has been modified a little in recent years. Some taxonomists, often called 'lumpers', prefer to stick to a simple description of a species and merely say that it shows some variation over its range. Others, known as 'splitters', prefer to separate these variations into what are known as sub-species and have modified Linnaeus's classification into a trinomial system. At least thirteen sub-species of Tawny Owl are now recognized. Reference to just three at this point will reveal how the trinomial system works.

1. *Strix aluco aluco* occurs throughout Scandinavia, Central and Eastern Europe.

2. *Strix aluco mauritanica* occurs in North Africa, Syria and Israel.

3. *Strix aluco sylvatica* occurs in Britain and Western Europe.

These sub-species evolve by interbreeding among populations which have little or no contact with other isolated groups, thus allowing minor variations to develop into recognisable features. This goes to show that evolution is not a static process but a dynamic one which should keep natural scientists continually on their toes looking for new variations. Add to this the fact that there are bound to be new species awaiting discovery, and it is clear that the owl file can never be closed.

Little Owl *(Athene noctua) brings a Cockchafer beetle to its young. The nest is in the roof of a derelict building.*

CHAPTER THREE

The Folklore of Owls

'The jelous swan, ayenst hys deth that singeth
The oule eke, that of deththe bode bringeth'

Geoffrey Chaucer (1343-1400)
The Parliament of Fowls

This quotation is one of many written examples of humans' underlying fear of owls, which seems to date back to a time before recorded history.

It is highly probable that owls would be among the first birds to be noticed by ancient man, probably because its vocalisations in the dead of night would cause havoc in the superstitious mind. Owls are certainly illustrated in cave paintings.

We are a diurnal species and are therefore uneasy when lost in the dark. Imagine an ancient Celt wandering around in a forest as darkness is falling on a chill winter's evening. Where, he wonders, are the wolves, wild boar and brown bears? Where also is home and the warm fire? Too soon it is dark and the terrified wanderer crashes his way through a tangle of bramble beneath an ivy-covered oak. What effect the sudden eruption of a resting deer or roosting heron would have we can only guess and if we then introduce the silent flight of an owl, with its shrieking call, we have the perfect recipe for panic. That the owl should become a symbol of death should hardly surprise us. When owls are so cosmopolitan, it is not surprising, looking at the literature of the ancient civilisations, to find that most share the same basic fear of owls as prophets of doom.

Just as for the Celt, ancient Greek religious beliefs also centred on the natural world, and gods were often given half-animal, half-human shapes and character-istics. Athene, the Little Owl is still called *Athene noctua*. This was initially a crow-based deity, but later the owl took over. The Little Owl was, in fact, very common around Athens, but considering that it is more diurnal than many other species, it may not have been quite so terrifying. The goddess changed her role over the centuries. Being first, in charge of 'thunder and lightning', she gradually evolved into a goddess of war and wisdom. These two characteristics are explained by the fact that owls are efficient and silent killers and yet the shape of their head and their stance are suprisingly reminiscent of the human body.

Birds have a problem when flying because strong winds blowing directly at them would make vision difficult. This is corrected by the presence of the nictitating membrane which is a sort of third eyelid functioning like a windshield. Most birds blink by sliding this membrane and their eyelids from side to side, but owls operate the system up and down. They therefore blink like we do and can also sometimes look sleepy or perhaps contemplative — hence the owl as a symbol of wisdom. Perhaps Athene also became known as the goddess of thriftiness, because there was a coin with her head on one side and that of an owl on the other. These coins were actually called 'owls'.

The ambivalent attitude to owls during the progress of human history can be seen from Biblical references. During his 'conversations' with God, Moses was made aware of which creatures could be eaten, the classifica-tion being that the consumption of finned, scaled, cud-chewing and cloven-hooved creatures was allowable, but with a number of exceptions. Some of these are clearly listed in the Old Testament book of Leviticus and it seems that birds suspected or proved to be flesh eaters, whether of live prey or carrion, were 'an abomination: the eagle and the ossifrage and the osprey . . . the owl . . . and the hawk after his kind. And the little owl and the cormorant, and the great owl'. It should not escape our attention that none of the birds listed would be on a gourmet's shopping list today and even the Romans, who had no such list of 'abominable foods' avoided eating owls, preferring the more sophisticated taste of pheasant and wildfowl. The Old Testament also indicates, especially in the doleful writings of Isaiah, the association between disaster and owls. In Isaiah 34: 11-15 we read the tale of a scene of destruction.

'The cormorant and the bittern shall possess it; the owl also and the raven shall dwell in it; and he shall stretch out upon it the line of confusion, and the stones of emptiness . . . And thorns shall come up in her palaces, nettles and brambles in the palaces thereof . . . and it shall be a court for owls. The wild beast of the desert shall also meet with the wild beasts of the island, and the satyr shall cry to his fellow; the screech owl shall also rest there, and find for herself a place of rest. There shall the great owl make her nest, and lay, and hatch, and gather under her shadow . . .'

The Roman Empire is famous for producing few innovations and yet possessing the ability to absorb the culture of all races with whom they made contact to produce an amalgam which still impresses the world today. In architecture they copied the Greeks, incorporated the Egyptian, studied the Hebrew and produced the glory that was Rome. Who would they follow in their dealings with the owl? Would Athene be a Jekyl or a Hyde? There is no doubt that evil won — the Roman goddess Minerva was based on the Greek goddess Athene, and the reputation of the wise old owl was destroyed forever. Pliny the Elder (AD 23-79) compiled a Roman natural history which is beautifully described in the *Oxford Companion to English Literature* (1985) as an 'enclyclopaedic rag-bag of popular science'. His writings do owls no favours at all.

'The scritch-owle betokeneth always some heavy news, and is most execrable and accursed in the presaging of public affairs. He keepeth ever in the deserts and loveth not only such unpeopled places, but also that are horribly hard of access. In sum he is the very monster of the night, neither crying nor singing out clear, but uttering a certain groan of doleful moaning. And, therefore, if he be seen either within cities or otherwise abroad in any place, it is not for good, but prognosticates some fearful misfortune.'

One might have assumed from this account that Pliny would have kept his eyes skinned for the sight of an owl in a city. Had he done so he might even have saved his own life because he was among those who perished when Mount Vesuvius erupted in AD 79, overwhelming the city of Pompeii near Naples. Despite Pliny's shortsightedness, the Romans continued to look on owls as harbingers of disaster.

Whenever the owl hooted, death was sure to follow and it is written that the Emperor Augustus's death was so predicted, and that when another of the emperors, this time Commodus Aurelius, was dying it is said that an owl entered the room and perched itself to witness the sad event. When one considers that there would have been a lot of owls about and that their sounds must have been quite familiar, it is a wonder that the Roman Empire survived as long as it did! As Shakespeare reported, Julius Caesar not only needed the 'Beware the Ides of March', he should also have avoided listening to the screech of the owl, which was said to have predicted his imminent death.

Perhaps the owl legends influenced others besides Shakespeare; they certainly loom large in Arab folklore. Here the owl is depicted as the spirit of people who have died unavenged — a truly dreadful state of affairs in Arab culture. It is no wonder the Arabs were frightened of owls because it was believed that they flew about at night on a vengeful hunt for the blood of those involved in their death. The dracula-like bird was even thought to cry out its desire for blood. In Arabic the soul of the departed was called the *sada,* or echo, and the dead were called *hama* and *sata.*

In Ethiopia they took the connection between the owl and death one step further. When a person on trial was found guilty of a capital offence, he or she was first shown a table on which an owl was painted and then made to commit suicide.

The connection between Jewish, Roman and Arab cultures can easily be made, but the Aborgines of Australia and the indigenous Red Indians of North America also developed a totally independent belief in the association between owls and death. It obviously has to do with the fact that death, darkness and owls are associated. In Australia Aboriginal folklore wove all three together and it was thought that the souls of men passed into bats and those of women into owls. Both

African Marsh Owl *(Otus capensis)*

bats and owls were therefore left well alone and never persecuted. Like that of the Australian Aborigines, Red Indian culture was also 'wildlife based' and many tribes believed that the bridge between life and death was controlled by the owl and that all souls on their way to the next world had to cross the owl bridge. The Kiowas believed that after death their medicine man became an owl and the owl itself, after death, took up the lesser life of a cricket. In the *Journal of American Folklore*, the creation of owls is described according to Red Indian tradition:

The husband of a young girl bought a small hut for her mother beside his hunting lodge. He killed many beaver, and while he and his wife cooked and ate the intestines, her mother cooked and ate the meat. The old woman, however, craved the intestines, because they had a lot of fat. One day she said to her daughter, 'Come with me and gather birch-bark for baskets.' They found a large birch-tree, and the mother stayed on the ground while the girl climbed to remove the bark. Then the old woman said to her, 'My daughter, say *hu hu* and fly away.' The girl refused, but at her mother's urging she at last said *hu hu* and fluttered her hands. Immediately she changed to an owl and flew away, only her skin remaining in the birch tree. Her mother then climbed the tree, put on her daughter's skin and returned to the camp.

When the young man came back from his hunting, he mistook the old woman for his wife and gave her the intestine of a beaver to cook. When it was cooked he ate one end of it while she ate the other, but, being toothless, her chewing made no noise. He said to her, ' I do not hear you eating.' And she answered. 'Today I was chewing birch-bark and my teeth are no good.' When they had finished their meal, he gave her some meat and told her to give it to her mother, but the old woman secretly threw it into the woods.

After they had gone to bed, his wife flew on top of the house and called '*hu hu* - You are sleeping with your mother-in-law. The youth, who was already suspicious, realised at once what had happened and tried to capture his wife, calling, 'I love you. Come back and be my wife again.' But she answered, 'I cannot return, for I have already changed to an owl.' And she flew away among the trees. He went back and killed his mother-in-law, then followed after his wife entreating her to return to him. She said to him, 'I cannot return, my husband. But you too say *hu hu* and fly.' As he repeated the words and fluttered his hands, his skin also dropped from him and the two owls flew away together. Thus owls originated in the world.

My favourite Red Indian story, however, was part of the folklore of the Chippewa tribe. They believed that the hooting of the Horned Owl foretold bad weather. The north wind was said to be produced by the owl, while the warm gentle wind from the south was produced by the butterfly. One can certainly see the sense in the association.

A pair of Tawny Owls inhabit a large yew tree in my garden. Their breeding cycle begins as early as February when they are very vocal. The noise seems louder on cold silent nights before the wind brings the snow. One can see how the Chippewas, shivering in their lodges, longed for the owl to be quiet and for the butterfly's, wings to generate the soft summer breezes.

In China also there is a great deal of folklore surrounding owls and this time the people seem to have reverted to the connection between owls and storms of thunder and lightning, just like the original Greek view of Athena. The four corners of Chinese houses often had owls carved on them to ward off lightning and dead owls were even nailed over the portals for the same reason. It has also been suggested that, in Britain, holes were left at convenient levels in barn walls to encourage the birds to enter and ward off lightning. It seems much more likely, however, that they were encouraged in to keep down vermin.

Ancient medicine made a great deal of use of bits and pieces taken from animals, including birds. It was thought that 'powdered owl', applied as an ointment, was the ideal cure for eye complaints. The ash obtained by burning owls' feet was taken as a powder against snake bite. This is not quite as silly as it sounds because owls kill with their feet and their legs, feathering also gives some protection against mammal bites, so people might be justified in thinking it would be just as effective against snakes. There seems to be less sense in the belief that the heart and right foot of an owl, when carefully placed on a sleeping person, worked as a truth drug.

With all this folklore to go on it is no wonder that literary folk made free use of owls in their writings. Shakespeare, no mean naturalist, made use of Roman authors and in *Julius Caesar* he writes of the emperor's impending death:

Yesterday the bird of night did sit,
Even at noonday, upon the market-place
Hooting and shrieking

In *Henry VI*, however, the bard shows his knowledge of the natural history of his native land:

The owl by day
If he arise, is mocked and wondered at

This is a clear reference to what has been called 'mobbing'. This is defined as the attacking of a predator at its roost by an assortment of small birds, presumably to drive it out of the area at a time when it is at its least efficient — the owl by day, for example.
Shakespeare, who is said to have fled from Charlecote, near Stratford-upon-Avon in Warwickshire, to London to avoid arrest for poaching deer, would have been well versed in the ways of the woodland both by day and by night.
In *A Midsummer Night's Dream* he writes:

The screech owl, screeching loud
Puts the wretch that lies in woe
In rememberance of a shroud

Here we have the association with death and we also find the supernatural stressed in *A Comedy of Errors*.

This is the fairy lord, O spite of spites
We talk with goblins and elvish sprites

Two more quotes from the Bard should establish his credentials as both naturalist and classical scholar. In *Macbeth* he notes that:

It was the owl that shrieked, the fatal bellman
Which gives the stern'st goodnight

In *Hamlet* Ophelia speaks the words 'They say the owl was a baker's daughter.' This refers to an ancient legend, possibly with its roots in Gloucestershire. Apparently Jesus went into a baker's shop and the man's wife put a cake into the oven to bake for him. Her greedy daughter thought the cake too big and cut it in half. The dough then swelled up to an enormous size and the greedy lass shouted 'hough hough hough' and was transmuted into an owl!

CHAPTER FOUR

Barn Owls and Bay or
Grass Owls

There are twelve species in the Tytonidae family, which are distinguished from the more numerous *Otus* owls of the Strigidae family by having a heart-shaped facial disc, long legs and a serrated comb on the claw of the middle toe. While taxonomists continue to debate precise classification, both with regard to names and the designation of sub-species, the present situation is summarised in table three. In the space available it is not possible to describe all twelve species in detail, and, in any event, some have only been studied at a very superficial level. At the other end of the spectrum, few species of bird have been more fully documented than the cosmopolitan Barn Owl. The Grass Owl of South Africa, although more restricted in range, also requires some attention since it is very much under threat, mainly due to the reduction of its habitat.

Barn Owl
(*Tytus alba*)

Barn Owls, vary a great deal, thus accounting for their separation into around 38 sub-species (see Table four), they all tend to be around 350mm (14.5 in) long and may be described as medium-sized owls. On average females tend to be slightly larger than their mates, but there is so much of an overlap that any distinction of gender on this basis is likely to be at best blurred and at worst totally unreliable. While the body length is average for an owl, the wing span is certainly impressive and is around 760 mm (30 in).

With regard to the plumage, the upper parts are orange-buff, speckled with grey and white (females do seem to be greyer) with the underside white with just a few dark grey spots. The heart-shaped face, which lacks ear tufts, thus adding to the rounded effect, is white with a rust-coloured border. At times the white bill is surrounded so completely by feathers that it is almost invisible — but not so the rather small black eyes which contrast sharply with the rest of the pale facial region.

The legs are long and feathered down to the dark brown feet which end in very powerful-looking claws, the killing equipment of the bird. When Barn Owls are about to be handled they tend to lean backwards and strike hard with their powerful talons, as many over-keen bird ringers have found to their cost. To perch, Barn Owls place two toes in front and two behind, but if moving about on a flat surface — say, a beam in a barn — they spread the toes evenly and achieve an excellent balance. Perhaps the shape of the tail may also help when moving in a confined space, since it ends in a V, in contrast to other European species of owl which have rounded tails.

No bird species has a wider distribution than the Barn Owl. In Europe it occurs as far north as Scotland (although it is absent from northern and eastern Scotland as well as the Hebrides), southern Sweden and the south west of the USSR. It also occurs in almost every other continent, which accounts for the large number of sub-species: it is found in much of Africa including Madagascar, throughout the Indian subcontinent, Malaysia and Australia. Both North and South America play host to a race of Barn Owl and the only continent not to have the species is Antarctica. In Britain the most common sub-species is the White-breasted Barn Owl (*Tyto alba alba*) which is dominant in south-west Europe, western France and Britain. The dark-breasted sub-species *Tyto alba guttata* gets its name from its dark spotted breast, since the Latin for a spot is *gutta*; this dominates the north and east of Europe including Sweden, Holland and Germany, throughout the Alpine region and into Poland, the western provinces of the USSR, Hungary and Bulgaria. The dark-breasted form has been recorded in Britain, especially when cold winters strike the eastern areas of Europe, while in some areas of France, Belgium and Germany the ranges of the two sub-species overlap. Should cross-breeding occur, there is no intermediate form, the two forms remaining genetically discrete, and seemingly co-dominant.

The distribution and history of the Barn Owl in Britain is fascinating. Barn Owls have been present here since the ice age (the Pleistocene period) some two million years ago. The thorough work on avian bones which was carried out by Colin Harrison in the 1980's shows that although the Barn Owl has been widespread throughout Britain, it is not very tolerant of extreme cold — unlike the Snowy Owl — and this may well still restrict its distribution in Scotland and northern Scandinavia. The effect of climate upon the species may account for the fluctuations in distribution which are still evident today.

During the early part of the nineteenth century there was a decline, probably due to persecution by game-keepers and the increased efficiency of firearms and availability of poisons. The demand for stuffed specimens of this attractive species also played an ignominious part in its decline. This continued into the present century, but the climate then seems to have warmed up slightly, resulting in an increase which, from the 1940s onwards, was reversed again by colder winters, loss of habitat, toxic chemicals picked up from their prey and the large numbers of Barn Owls killed by faster moving and increased levels of traffic on the roads. The population is now estimated to be in the range of 5,000 to 9,000 pairs and the situation may well be getting worse.

It is in this worrying climate that British conservationists have taken a hand. Barn Owls found injured (usually road traffic casualties) are repaired but are often unfit to be released into the wild. They are, however, perfectly able to breed and the resulting offspring can then be released. Many naturalists, the author included, have been surprised at the eagerness of farmers to restore the owls to barns which have not been occupied for many years. Release schemes have to be carefully organised, however captive-bred birds have to be taught to hunt and must be protected as they begin to breed themselves. All involved in these schemes should be fully aware of the Barn Owl's requirements and biology.

Barn Owls prefer open farmland and are therefore not in competition with the Tawny Owl which requires a greater degree of tree cover. On the whole, Barn Owls are nocturnal, but in very cold weather or when there are young to be fed, the hunting period may have to be extended well into the daylight hours, and also may begin long before dark. For roosting sites, buildings and cliffs may be chosen, and even hollow trees are attractive. Single birds or pairs may select a roost and there are also a few records of group roosts, but some workers think this occurs mainly when good roosting sites are at a premium.

Watching barn owls hunting is one of the most exciting events in the birdwatcher's calendar. I have watched them working from a perch on a mill town's gasometer, from a church tower in a cathedral city, from a farmer's barn in the Yorkshire Dales and from an old abbey in Galloway — the technique is always the same. They quarter the ground with a flight which is so relaxed that it is easy to forget one is watching one of the most efficient killers in the natural world. Once prey is located, they hover quite close to the ground and then drop quickly, talons outstretched, and carry off their victim.

Barn, and many other owls, are able to hunt by ear; even in total darkness. Barn Owls feed mainly on rodents, but they have been seen beating their wings against the foliage of trees, especially those covered with ivy, in order to flush out small birds roosting there.

The list of prey items is long and David Glue, of the British Trust of Ornithology, has made a thorough study of Barn Owl pellets. Such studies have been invaluable in proving that the Barn Owl is no threat whatever to those who rely for their living upon raising game birds for the shooting fraternity. Glue analysed the contents of 165 Barn Owl pellets from Oxfordshire,

Barn Owl *(Tyto alba) with shrew*

Barn Owl   *(Tyto alba)*

vocal compared with species like the Tawny Owl, but males do greet their mates with a squeaking call, the females replying with a sound rather like human snoring. I was once called out by my local policeman to identify a sound he had been summoned to investigate by a farmer's wife who had reported a vagrant asleep in her barn. He failed to find such a large species, but between us we found an amorous female owl sitting close to a water downspout which acted like an amplifier.

This 'snoring' persuades the male to present food to his mate who then allows him to copulate with her. As many as eleven eggs may be laid in years when prey items are in good supply, but the average clutch is about half of this number, and in some years, when conditions are particularly adverse, egg laying may not occur at all.

The site chosen for the egg laying is variable, but no nest is actually constructed. In barns, the white, rough-textured elliptically shaped eggs (unusual in owls where the eggs are nearly always spherical) are usually laid onto a mat of disgorged pellets or rotting wood.

Very occasionally the wood may contain luminous bacteria and these may become embedded in the bird's plumage — when it takes off the glow can create a very ghostly effect and probably accounts for the Barn Owl's sinister reputation. In other cases the nests of other species, particularly the crow family, which are about the right size, are taken over by the owls.

The eggs are laid at two — or even three-day intervals and incubation, by the female only, begins at once and results in an asynchronous hatching and considerable variations in size of the young in the nest. This may occasionally lead, in times of food shortage, to the stronger eating the weaker. Although this may appear somewhat grisly, there is no doubting its survival value, since it is better that some should survive at the expense of others.

Although the male plays no part in the 32-34-day incubation period, he does provide his mate with food throughout her stint and takes his full share of feeding the young. In periods when there is plenty of food available, two broods may be raised and the parents are kept really busy feeding as many as a dozen hungry young which fledge in about two months and leave the parents' territory after twelve weeks. In view of this reproductive efficiency, it is a wonder that the species has declined, but at least it must give us optimism for its future. So must the life expectancy of the Barn Owl which, in captivity, can live for twenty years, although

England and identified 42,375 vertebrate items. He found that only 2 per cent of these were avian and that the bulk of the food consisted of Short-tailed Field Voles (*Microtus agrestis*), Common Shrews (*Sorex araneus*), Wood Mice (*Apodemus sylvaticus*) and even Brown Rats (*Rattus norvegicus*).

The Cheshire naturalist T. A. Coward reported in 1946 that a captive Barn Owl fed regularly on rats which were swallowed whole, the tail actually protruding from the bill while the body was being digested. I myself observed a Barn Owl in Cumbria catch, decapitate and swallow a Weasel (*Mustela nivalis*) in January 1981. Decapitation of prey does seem to be a feature of Barn Owl feeding, particularly during the breeding season, which, in Britain, begins in April or May.

Once a pair have become established, it is quite likely that they will remain together for life. They are mature at the end of their first year, the first sign of adult behaviour being the screeching of the males to claim their territory. This they often do whilst in flight and some workers have suggested that they also have a 'wing clapping' ceremony. Barn Owls are not particularly in the wild half this period would seem to be more accurate.

Grass Owl
(*Tyto capensis*)

Male and female Grass Owls are similar in appearance. The length of the body varies from 34-37 cm (14½ in). The bill is white and the legs yellow. It is somewhat larger and darker on the dorsal surface — some workers reporting that it is almost black — than the Barn Owl. There is no barring on the tail, while the face is rounder and darker than the rest of the head and this makes it look as if the bird is wearing a cap. Young birds can be identified by a more golden-yellow plumage below and more rufus coloration on the face. Grass Owls can produce loud noises, but seem to prefer to remain silent. When provoked, however, they produce a snake-like hissing which must be very disconcerting to predators.

The South African Grass Owl is becoming something of a rare species, partly due to its preference for moist expanses of grassland, areas only found in the eastern half of the subcontinent. At one time it was suggested that it occurs in northern Namibia, but experts on the species have now firmly rejected this theory. It does have very special requirements, and suitable areas are declining, especially in Zimbabwe which is still, however, its main territory.

There is no doubt that the Grass Owl and the Barn Owl are closely related, but they are prevented from coming into direct competition by having clearly defined differences with regard to habitat preferences. *Tyto capensis* frequents areas of long grass alongside streams, but will also breed in damp, lightly wooded country. It would appear that the Marsh Owl *(Asio capensis)* is a more worrying competitor, but the Grass Owl does have a longer bill, longer legs and more powerful feet and claws, which enable it to kill larger prey. Most students of African avifauna feel that more research is required in this difficult area of owl biology. Field workers, however, think that the two species may employ different hunting techniques, which means that they tap a slightly different group of prey items. Marsh Owls tend to sweep over large areas and to pounce rather than settling down. In contrast, the Grass Owl covers less ground, but settles far more often and

Heraldic attitude of a Barn Owl *(Tyto alba) flying into a Suffolk barn with a vole in its bill.*

searches the area much more thoroughly. The Marsh Owl also has longer wings with a pale area near the tips, which enables experienced field workers to distinguish the two species.

The prey includes insects, especially termites, but this may well be a case of the birds not looking a gift-horse in the mouth. During the rainy season these termites are common, as are other invertebrates and amphibians which thrive in wetter conditions. Birds are actively hunted, the preferred order being passerines, although members of the pigeon family frequently appear on the menu of the Grass Owl. The main prey, however, consists of mammals, particularly the abundant member of the rat family, *Vlei otomys*.

Eggs have been found in each month between December and August, but the breeding season peaks between February and April. The rainfall at this period controls the growth of grass, which is essential to provide protective cover for the nest. The way that much of the land in the breeding area is managed, involving burning off the grass cover during the winter, can cause problems.

The eggs are similar in shape to those of the Barn Owl, but there are important differences between the two species with regard to clutch size and incubation strategy. The usual clutch size of the Grass Owl is between three and five (six is the maximum recorded), a much smaller number than that of the Barn Owl. The incubation period was given as 42 days by Roberts, but

Peter Steyn suggests 32 days and obviously more work is required to establish the period with certainty. Unlike the Barn Owl, the Grass Owl begins its incubation on the completion of the clutch, thus ensuring that the young all hatch at the same time. Despite this, however, some workers have reported considerable variation in both size and weight of the owlets.

If the Grass Owl is under threat, we should be even more concerned about the possible fate of other species of the Tytonidae, five of the twelve species being listed as among the rare birds of the world.

The Madagascar Grass Owl
(*Tyto soumagnei*)

This species is also known as the Red Owl. It was first described in 1874 and since then the number of reliable sightings have been few and far between. Only the rain forest area in the eastern central region of Madagascar would seem to be a suitable area, yet this owl has only been seen here once in the last 50 years. This (1973) sighting may well have been the last and we must accept the possibility that the Red Owl may already be lost to us for ever.

Madagascar, once famous for the variety of its avifauna, is now the black spot of world ornithology. Birds were ruthlessly hunted for feathers, zoos and museums, as many species were unique to the island and the world's scientists were reluctant to resist the temptation to collect attractive specimens. Add to this the fact that 80 per cent of the once-extensive forests have been removed to bolster the island's weak economy and it is easy to understand the problems faced by birds such as the Red Owl. We cannot be too optimistic since almost 30 other species have the same problem.

Other Species

The Taliabu owl or Black Brown Barn Owl (*Tyto nigrobrunneg*) is only known from a single specimen from Taliabu, Indonesia, while the Minahassa Owl (*Tyto inexpectata*) is not well known either, apart from the fact that it is considered a rarity in Sulawesi, Indonesia. The Golden Owl (*Tyto aurantia*) seems to be confined to the dense rain forests of New Britain where the birds are difficult to observe closely.

Finally, we have to consider the Itombue or Congo Bay Owl (*Phodilus prigoginei*) whose rarity is underlined by the fact that only one specimen is available — a bird taken in 1953, whilst roosting in long grass in the Itombue mountains to the east of Zaire. There was another sighting of the mystery bird in 1971 and the Government of Zaire have reacted sensibly by producing a conservation plan for this area of forest. Perhaps this should be our approach to the preservation of these rarities; to a certain extent this could apply to the Barn Owl and the Grass Owl too. Perhaps we should spend our energies and finances on the preservation of habitat and let the rare species enjoy this and look after themselves. They were, after all, doing this for thousands of years before human greed disturbed the balance of the environment.

Scops Owl   (*Otus scops)*

CHAPTER FIVE

The Otus Owls

The species described in this chapter come from the family Strigidae and are part of the sub-family Buboniae. The classification is complicated, to say the least, especially relating to birds from the area around Indonesia, and the list which follows seems to be in a continual state of flux, although some sense of order is now gradually becoming apparent, with some 41 species recognised. (I always find it handy to have either a good modern atlas or a globe to hand when studying the distribution of species and sub-species.)

The White-fronted Scops Owl
(*Otus sagittatus*)

This owl occurs in southern Burma, Thailand, Malaysia and possibly Sumatra. There are no sub-species. Its favoured habitat is apparently lowland forest, but there are few sightings of this very rare bird and no recordings or description of its voice. There may, therefore, be more individual owls present than has so far been calculated.

The Rufus or Reddish Scops Owl
(*Otus rufescens*)

This owl is at present thought to have three sub-species. The nominate race, *Otus rufescens rufescens*, is resident in Sumatra, Java and Borneo, while *Otus rufescens malyensis* is, as its name implies, restricted to Malaysia. *Otus rufescens burbidgei* is restricted to Jolo Island.

The Sandy or Cinnamon Scops Owl
(*Otus icterorhynchus*)

This is divided into two sub-species, the nominate *Otus icterorhynchus icterorhynchus* from Ghana, and *Otus icterorhynchus holerythrus* which occurs from South Cameroon to northern Zaire.

Sokoke Scops Owl
(*Otus ireneae*)

This owl has no sub-species and occurs in the south-east region of Kenya. It is also known as Mrs Morden's Owlet. This miniature species was only discovered in 1965 in the Sokaki forest along the coast of Kenya. The forest in this area is under threat of felling and if this occurs the population, currently estimated at around 2,000 pairs, is doomed. A small — some say too small —reserve has been created under Kenyan law and the Sokoke Scops Owl is also protected under the ICBP Endangered Species list. What is needed is a thorough research of its biology as it is only when conservationists are armed with this that they can be expected to do their best work.

The Spotted Scops Owl
(*Otus spilocephalus*)

This has as many as nine sub-species which are summarised in Table 5. Very little is known about the biology of any of these races.

The Andaman Scops Owl
(*Otus balli*)

This is a small caterpillar-eating owl which is restricted to the Andaman islands and has no sub-species.

Flores or Everett's Owl
(*Otus alfredi*)

This is represented only by the nominate species, and little is known about it except its preference for mountainous forests. Only three specimens have ever been examined, all taken during the nineteenth century from the Flores region of Indonesia. It may well be extinct, but for the moment it remains listed among the living species.

The Striated Scops Owl
(*Otus brucei*)

At one time not all taxonomists accepted this as a separate species, but preferred to add it to the continually expanding number of sub-species of the Common Scops Owl (*Otus scops*). In recent years, however, field studies have confirmed its right to a listing as a separate species, with six sub-species of its own. (These are listed in Table 6.) This species averages something over 20 cm (8 in) in length, with a wing span of about 60 mm (24 in) and is therefore a little larger than the Common Scops Owl. The two species are distinguishable in several particulars, but the Striated Scops Owl is especially obvious in having a greyer plumage with no rufous shades at all. There are no white spots, either on the crown or the back of the neck, and the streaks and vermiculations are both fainter and finer.

Although both species have spots on the scapulars, these are less obvious in the Striated Scops Owl, the underparts of which are also markedly paler, as is the area surrounding the eye. The distribution of the two species does overlap and even experienced owl students admit that they find distinction between the two in the field — especially in dim light — very difficult. The Striated Scops produces a series of 'wup-wup-wup' sounds, which are much quicker and perhaps softer than those of the Common Scops.

The favoured habitat is riverside forests in warm dry areas of the western Palaearctic, but is has also proved to be attracted to gardens and parks, especially when willow and poplar trees grow in abundance. It tends not to be too happy in mountainous regions, but in Pakistan it has been recorded in stony foothills up to a height of 1,800 m (5,900 ft).

This owl will hunt by day but is mostly nocturnal, spending the daylight hours in dense foliage or pressed hard against a tree trunk. It is perfectly camouflaged for this purpose, which may well account for the spots on the plumage. The eggs are laid during April and May, in a nest which may have been that of a Magpie (*Pica pica*), a hole in a tree, riverbank, building or even in a nest box. The preferred height seems to be between 3 and 10 metres (10 -32½ ft) and some workers have suggested that the owl may repair an old nest or add a lining, but these facts have not been proved with certainty.

The smooth, white, slightly glossy eggs average 31 × 28 mm (1.2 × 1.1 in) and the clutch size varies from three to six. Incubation is by the female only and begins with the laying of the first egg, so the owlets vary considerably in size. The incubation period seems to be around 28 days and the young, which squeal rhythmically, are fed by both parents, leaving the nest about 30 days after hatching. The fledging period is also about 30 days. Little is known regarding the time at which they are independent of the parents or the age of first breeding; it is likely, however, that they will breed in the first spring following their birth.

The diet is varied which, apart from their unusually confiding nature, may account for the fact that they are easily tamed. They have been known to catch moths and bats on the wing. The bounding flight of the Striated Scops is very exciting to watch and almost equal in elegance to that of a falcon. Insects, amphibians, lizards, birds and small mammals are all taken from the ground or by dropping on them suddenly from a convenient perch. There are many records of the species being aware that artificial lights attract both moths and bats, and waiting in suitable places to ambush their prey.

The Common Scops Owl
(*Otus scops*)

So far at least 21 sub-species are 'split' from the main stem (see table 6). The sub-species found throughout Western Europe, to Russia and southern China, is *Otus scops scops* and this will now be described in detail as typical of the genus. In fact this owl is the only representative of the genus to be found in Europe which only occurs as a breeding species south of 47° north. This region includes Portugal and Spain, the southern half of France, Italy, Yugoslavia, Greece and the Balkans. It is also common in the Atlas region of North Africa, Turkey and parts of the south and west of the USSR. The birds found in southern China are somewhat isolated, which has persuaded some workers to treat them as a separate species which they call *Otus sunia*. This is not, however, the majority opinion among ornithologists. As we shall see later, the diet of the Scops Owl is almost entirely insectivorous and it is therefore more migratory than many owl species. Insects do not thrive in cold weather. During periods of strong equinoctial winds this owl can be driven into areas outside its breeding range, including Scandinavia and Britain, but these visits are never regular and the Scops is a rare vagrant in such areas.

Only about 19 cm (7½in), the Scops is a small owl, the females being very slightly larger than the males. This lack of bulk is further stressed by the owl's slim shape and small head. The latter feature makes the bright yellow eyes look particularly huge even for an owl. A friend of mine once described his first view of a Scops as like seeing a small sports car with huge headlights. The small head, plus the presence of ear tufts and a longer tail, distinguish the Scops from the more dumpy Little Owl.

The upperparts are basically greyish-brown, but are fringed with rufous-brown at the edge of the mantle and the sides of the facial disc. The rufous feathers around the fascial disc look as if they have been traced round in black by a skilful artist with a fine brush. The underparts are pale grey and there tends to be streaking on the breast. Both the flight feathers and retrices are barred with grey or buff on white. The bill is black and, unusually among owls, the yellowish-brown feet are not feathered. The sexes tend to be similar, but there are two distinct colour phases. Those owls with a basic grey plumage seem to realise this and roost hard up against the trunks of trees, while those individuals which have more rufous-red in their plumage, choose thick foliage or even autumn colouring.

The breeding call — would it be wrong to call the noise a song? — has been likened to that of a Redshank (*Tringa totanus*) and this was certainly my impression on my first hearing. The sound is very low; a sort of disyllabic whistling which is repeated for hours and just as monotonously as the chirping of a cricket. There are also occasions when the listener is treated to a duet as a pair face each other in a tree — experts can distinguish the call of the female, which is higher pitched and not as regular as that of the male. After this mutual serenade the male conducts the female on a tour of what he feels are suitable nest holes before she selects the preferred site. This is usually in a tangle of broadleaved trees with cork oak and date palms being among the most favoured. Abandoned nests of members of the crow family may be taken over and, on occasions, walls and ruined buildings may be chosen, the preferred height being from 1-12 m (3¼-39 ft) from the ground.

The female incubates the clutch of between three and six eggs, laid at two-day intervals, for a period of around 23 days. She remains in complete charge of the owlets until they are 18 days old, but the male is an attentive partner, bringing a regular supply of food. There are times when the male may have to work very hard because he sometimes has two mates, both with a brood to feed. Both sexes are very fierce in defence of the nest and young. After the eighteenth day, the male also feeds the chicks and the youngsters can usually fly from the thirty-third day following hatching. The family group tends to remain together during migration, but the youngsters are able to breed by the age of nine months.

They may well disperse either before or during the return migration. Work done by Koenig in 1973 suggests that males are unable to breed after the age of six, the females being fertile until they are about ten. Ringing returns suggest a maximum life span of thirteen years.

Scops Owls hunt by night, but are more diurnal in habit than some owl species. They select a well-concealed roost and seem to 'wake-up' slowly, accompanying their rising with a series of high-pitched piping notes. The flight of the Scops is direct and rapid and after locating its prey from a perch the kill is quickly accomplished. Unlike large owls, which kill highly nutritious rodents, the small Scops is an insect feeder and so has to collect many more prey items to satisfy its energy requirements. In Germany and western Switzerland, according to Mebs (1966), the staple diet consists of Great Green Bush Crickets (*Tettigonia viridisimma*) which are apparently located more by sound than sight. Small mice, shrews and small birds, perhaps ailing individuals or fledgelings, are occasionally taken.

It would seem that the Scops Owl is the most insectivorous of the European owls. This fact makes their pellets more difficult to analyse. I see three reasons for this: first, pellets with hard dry insect exoskeletons tend to be very fragile; second, the pellets themselves are very small (20 - 25mm/0.8 - 1 in) and deposited into what is often tangled undergrowth; third, and perhaps just as important, there is a shortage of entomologists skilful enough to identify the shattered remnants of tiny creatures. Direct observation of the birds feeding remains the best evidence we have of their diet and in 1959 Meinertzhagen, working in Crete, reported Scops Owls taking quantities of the Oleander Hawk Moth (*Daphnis nerii)*.

While the Scops Owl is certainly regarded as a European owl, it is only a visitor over much of this continent and there is ample evidence to suggest that its range is shrinking southwards.

The Mentaur Scops Owl
(*Otus umbra*)

There are two sub-species. *Otus umbra umbra,* native to Simalur Island, and *Otus umbra enganensis* of Enggeno Island. These islands are situated off the south-west coast of Sumatra in the Indian Ocean.

The African Scops Owl
(*Otus senegalensis*)

This Owl is also known as the Cape Scops Owl, although the twelve sub-species occur over a substantial area of the continent (see Table 7). According to Peter Steyn in his book *A Delight of Owls — African Owls Observed* (1984), there is a great deal of work to be done on this species. He points out that:

'The Scops Owl lays from September to November, but there are few breeding records. The nest is usually a natural vertical hole in a tree. Two or three eggs are laid but the incubation period and other details of the breeding biology are unknown. As far as I know, the Scops Owl has been photographed only once at the nest by Alan Weaving in Rhodesia (now Zimbabwe). Unfortunately his observations were abruptly cut short when a Tree Monitor (or Leguaan) was found in the hole after eating either the eggs or small chicks. He established that at dusk the male called from his roost 120 metres from the nest before setting off to hunt. The male would come to the nest with insects and enter the hole to feed the female, or she would come up to the rim of the nest to take food from him . . . All the prey that he observed brought to the nest, or that he found in pellets, consisted of insects thus confirming that the Scops Owl seems to be entirely insectivorous.'

The species measures between 18 and 20 cm (7-8 in) and there is just a chance that it could be confused with the White-faced Owl (*Otus leucotis*) which is also small and has ear tufts (see below), but the Scops always has some degree of brown on the back, a grey face and is less obviously streaked on the upper surface. Both grey and brown phases have been identified and the sexes are alike. The iris of the eye is yellow and the bill and legs are bluish.

The Scops Owl is widely dispersed but not common. The voice is described as a 'purring chirruping trill'. Apparently the clutch size is three, but this figure is based upon very few records. A clutch of three white eggs was taken from northern Zululand. These measured 27 × 33 mm (1.06 × 1.3 in) but no further details are available at the time of writing.

The Flammulated Owl
(*Otus flammeolus*)

This species is represented by only two sub-species, the nominate *Otus flammeolus flammeolus,* occurring between south-west Canada and western Mexico, and the aptly named *Otus flammeolus rarus* from Guatemala. This is only about 18 cm (7 in) long. This bird is described by Peterson as the Flammulated Screech Owl. It is locally distributed, often quite rare, and confined to high tree-clad mountains. It is mainly grey in colour with just the odd touch of tawny. Rounded ear tufts are present but not very conspicuous. It is, however, the only species of owl in the region which has brown eyes.

Rajah's Scops Owl
(*Otus brookii*)

This species has been little studied, although it has now been divided into two sub-species. *Otus brookii brookii* occurs in Java and Borneo, while *Otus brookii solokensis* occurs in Sumatra.

The Madagascar Scops Owl
(*Otus rutilus*)

This is another little studied species, which is a great pity because of avifauna is perhaps more threatened in this area than anywhere else in the world. The tree cover is being harvested at a rate even more worrying than that of South America.

Three sub-species have been recognised. One, *Otus rutilus rutilus*, is confined to the island of Madagascar itself; the other two are isolated on smaller islands. These sub-species are *Otus rutilus pembaensis* of Pemba Island, and *Otus rutilus capnodes* which occurs on Anjouan Island.

Readers will have detected that the author is more of a 'lumper' than a 'splitter', but I can see why distinct sub-species can be recognised on and around Madagascar. The huge island has been isolated from Africa for so long that it has evolved its own fauna and flora and is thus a sort of living laboratory. It is tragic that it is being devastated by those from comparatively rich and greedy nations who demand cheap timber from Madagascar. They are reluctant to pour money into the region, as opposed to exploiting it, and thus the habitats of many unique species are being destroyed.

Madagascar was separated from Africa many millions of years ago. Initially both had similar wildlife and a comparison between present life forms may well provide an insight into the way species evolve. In the case of the Madagascar Scops Owl, some taxonomists feel that *Otus rutilus pembaensis* should be called the Russet Scops Owl (*Otus pembaensis*). Here again we see the dynamics of evolution at work, and the debate about, and the development of, ornithological knowledge should be exciting rather than frustrating. A further debating point concerns the Seychelles Owl (*Otus insularis*) which is sometimes considered to be a race of *Otus rutilus*. Taxonomists never seem quite in agreement as to whether this has or has not evolved into a separate species.

The Celebes Scops Owl
(*Otus manadensis*)

This owl has a discontinuous range among the islands of South East Asia in the region of Indonesia. This has led to the recognition of around thirteen sub-species (see Table 8), all based upon minor anatomical differences. Since this area is such a difficult and dangerous region in which to carry out fieldwork, there is a great deal we do not know, although basic habits and behaviour patterns are probably similar to those of the other, better known Scops Owls.

The taxonomic situation, however, remains far from satisfactory at the moment. Again we find argument as to whether the Biak Island or Misora Scops Owl (*Otus beccarii*) is actually conspecific (the same species) with *Otus manadensis*. Not enough specimens of either have yet been studied in order to find out. My own view is that we may need another sub-species (*Otus manadensis beccarii*) to describe the individuals found on Biak Island. Under its name *Otus beccarii*, however, the owl, again about 18 cm (7 in) long, is also said to occur in Grelvink Bay and Irian Jaya where it is apparently in danger of extinction. This is because its preferred habitat is the forest which is rapidly being exploited.

The Lesser Sunda or Flores Scops Owl
(*Otus sylvicola*)

This owl is restricted to the coastal forests of Flores and Sumbawa Islands. There are no sub-species.

The Collared Scops owl
(*Otus bakkamoena*)

This insect-eating species is found in forests around south and east Asia and Indonesia. With such a wide range, yet separated by large expanses of sea, it is perhaps not surprising to find that it has been 'split' into 23 sub-species (see Table 9).

Whitehead's Scops Owl
(*Otus whiteheadi)*

This owl is sometimes listed as a sub-species of *Otus bakkamoena* or of *Otus spilocephalus*, which underlines once more just how complex the taxonomy of this large order really is.

The Seychelles Owl or Bare-Legged Scops Owl
(*Otus insularis*)

This bird is now thought to be sufficiently 'insulated' to merit specific rank. One of the rarest of birds, with only about 80 pairs resident on Mahé, the bird has modestly improved its status since 1959 when it was thought to be extinct. The status of the species in 1980 was summarised by Jeff Watson who wrote one of the finest magazine articles I have ever read. It was published in *Wildlife Magazine* in May 1980:

'Few tropical islands have escaped man's destructive influence and Seychelles have proved no exception. Magnificent tropical forests have vanished with the demand for quality timber. Yet, on the island of Mahé, largest of the archipelago, areas of highland forest of great beauty and interest remain, and, up on the slopes of Morne Seychellois at night, one can enter a world that seems totally unchanged since man's arrival two hundred years ago.

Deforestation has brought casualties among the animal population as well as the trees. One native species, the Bare-legged Scops Owl, was thought to have been extinct for half a century when, in 1959, Philippe Lalanne found it in the mountains of south-central Mahé.

Seychelles has a dozen endemic land birds, but none as evasive as the Scops Owl. This is partly because of its strictly nocturnal habits, and also because of the nature of the country to which it is confined — luxuriant forest, shrouded in swirling mist for much of the year, and precipitous gradients, which would discourage all but the most determined owl-watcher.

In the years following Lalanne's discovery, few visiting naturalists were lucky enough to catch sight of this elusive bird, and when I arrived in the islands at the end of 1974 to begin a study of the ecology of the Seychelles kestrel, I was intrigued by the mystery surrounding the owl, and resolved to search for it.

I will never forget my first encounter with the bird. It came in the form of an extraordinary outburst of grunting from high in the forest canopy on a wet New Year's Eve.

For several months after that, my contact remained strictly auditory — short bursts of calling from birds in the canopy somewhere. Other people who heard the calls with me were sceptical that such strange vocal antics could be the work of a bird, let alone an owl.

My most important breakthrough happened on a fine September evening. All about me in the dark mountain forest were the plaintive peeping of tiny moss frogs, the buzz of cicadas, and the monotonous churring of crickets, which merged into a kind of natural symphony. Suddenly, a few yards away, an owl began its rhythmic calling. I set my tape recorder in motion. The bird continued to call and then flew away into the canopy.

I could now, I hoped, lure the bird from its hideout by playing back its voice.

The response was dramatic; it replied in less than 20 seconds. After calling for a few minutes, it stopped, but soon started again, this time much closer. It took only a moment or two to locate it with the powerful beam of my torch, and before long I saw the characteristic blunt-headed outline. Sitting motionless in the strong light, the owl leaned forward on its long, bare legs, peering at me through two enormous yellow eyes.

My next achievement was to be a "first" — the first good photograph of *Otus insularis* in the wild ever to be taken. My success was thanks to my tape recordings, which enabled me to observe hitherto unknown aspects of the owl's behaviour and posture. In aggressive mood, it stalks the offending tape recorder, body feathers puffed out, mantle feathers raised like the hackles on a dog's back, the body held close to horizontal so that the long, unfeathered legs are displayed and the head is held low, with no hint of ear tufts.

In complete contrast, a frightened bird held in the hand after capture for ringing shows sleeked body feathers and extended ear tufts. (For a long time it was believed that this owl lacked ear tufts — presumably because they are hardly ever raised by a wild bird at night.)

Although the advantage of the bird's long, bare legs remains a mystery, they seem to be helpful as it clambers, sometimes "hand and foot", through dense scrub in the lower levels of the forest, looking for lizards and insects.

I searched in vain for its nest in likely-looking holes in trees, which strengthens the argument that it builds in unusual sites. A speculative proposition is that it could build a subterranean nest, for unfeathered legs are a feature of a number of burrowing owls.

On the rare occasions that a pair is seen together, the birds may begin a display sequence as they approach one another in crouching posture along a branch. Then follows a period of intensified dueting, which ends when they briefly touch bills and one flies off.

The behaviour which leads to copulation is quite different. Male and female sit a few yards apart and calling builds up to a peak as the male flies in, mates and quickly flies off. Each copulation is accompanied by a high-pitched whistling call. The incidence of this whistle call varies throughout the year, occurring most frequently in October and again in April, leading to a tentative suggestion that there may be two breeding seasons annually. I have observed fledged youngsters in November and June.

The Creole name for the Scops Owl is *scieur* or sawyer and, at a distance, the rhythmic rasping call resembles a woodsman sawing. Other descriptions have been less complimentary: there was the doctor who diagnosed a bad case of bronchial pneumonia, until I pointed out that he was listening to the rarest owl in the world, whereupon he replied that, with a voice like that, it deserved to be on the critical list!

The relationships of the Seychelles Owl are obscure, but now it seems that, through a knowledge of its call,

there may be a clue. The typical call, of either sex, comprises a series of deep croaks or grunts at the rate of one a second, and may last for up to 20 minutes without rest. The voice of the African Scops Owl bears no resemblance to that of the Seychelles bird, and when I played a tape recording of the former to the latter it did not respond. Subsequently, I exchanged tapes with Dr Joe Marshall of the American Museum of Natural History, who had been working on an Indonesian Scops Owl. When I received his tape, I was amazed by its similarity to the call of the Seychelles bird, and the call of each species elicits a positive response from the other. So it looks as if the Seychelles Scops Owl has closer relatives in the Oriental region than on the African mainland.

My second discovery was that of a subtle voice difference between individual Seychelles owls. And this has been of particular interest as it has enabled the first realistic estimate of the number of this species to be made.

Guesses in the past have put the population at only 20. I would say that, at a conservative estimate, there are at least 80 pairs surviving in the highland forest of Mahé. And since much of this forest is now incorporated within the Morne Seychellois Natural Park, the long-term prospects for the species seem to be good.

On this revised estimate, it is doubtful whether the Seychelles Bare-legged Owl can, any longer, hold claim to the title "the rarest owl in the world" — and that can only be cause for celebration'.

The Screech Owl
(*Otus asio*)

Being a North American species, this owl has been studied very carefully and is divided into 22 sub-species (see Table 10). The nominate sub-species, *Otus asio asio*, occurs from East Virginia to Kansas. This small grey owl has prominent ear tufts which distinguish it from all other small Western owls within the size range of 20-25 cm (8 - 10 in). It prefers a well-wooded habitat, but as you move west it becomes less and less common. In New Mexico and the Texas Panhandle it is absent. Apart from breeding in woodlands, it seems quite prepared to tolerate human presence and nests have also been found in buildings, gardens, orchards and farmyards. Indeed, these owls are so small and inconspicuous that their presence may go completely undetected.

The wailing call is distinctive, as are a series of short calls building up to a trill, which I have heard likened to a small ball bouncing to a standstill. The Screech Owl will accept artificial nest boxes, especially if a little sawdust has been laid inside. Like most owls, it seldom lines its nest and the sawdust in the box may help this to resemble its favourite site — a hole created by a woodpecker — which would also, inevitably, have loose chippings inside.

In Oklahoma and Kansas eggs are laid between mid-March and early May, while in the cooler climate of North Dakota the period is between mid-April and early June. The clutch size varies from two to seven, but four or five seem to be the normal number. The incubation period has been stated to vary from 21-30 days. I think that this discrepancy is accounted for by the fact that a clutch of four eggs takes eight days to complete, and while the female may roost on her nest to protect the eggs, she does not actually press her warm brood patch hard onto them until the clutch is complete. The true period is therefore probably in the range of 24 days.

The male plays no part in the incubation, although he does provide the female with food. While insects play a large part in the diet, the Screech Owl is a little larger than most of the owls in the *Otus* genus and so is able to broaden the spectrum of its diet. A. A. Allan observed a pair over a 45-day period during the breeding season and identified insects, mammals, crayfish (I wonder how they caught these?), salamanders and a total of 77 birds belonging to 18 species, including tanagers, phoebes, sparrows and warblers. By the time they are 30 days old, the young can fly, and are able to breed in the year following their birth.

The Spotted or Whiskered Screech Owl
(*Otus trichopsis*)

This owl is very similar in appearance to *Otus asio*, but can be distinguished by large white spots on the lower hind neck and scapular (shoulder) feathers, with even larger black spots on the underparts, plus the very long facial bristles from which the species takes its name. The voices of the two species are also very different, a point which is often overlooked by ornithologists.

Species can be kept discrete by sound differences just as easily as by visual differences. The Spotted Screech Owl produces a four-syllable call 'boobooboo-boo, boobooboo-bo', which is quite different from the bouncing-ball rhythm of the Common Screech Owl.

The two species are also separated by their choice of habitat, the Spotted Screech Owl being found among oak-lined canyons of the mountainous region of southern Arizona, between 1220 and 1980 m (4,000-6,500 ft). With such a wide distribution it is not surprising that the 'splitters' have recognised six sub-species (see Table 11), occuring between North America and El Salvador.

The Bearded Screech Owl
(*Otus barbarus*)

This owl occurs in Guatemala. It has no sub-species and there is little detailed documentation concerning its habits. The same applies to the following species, *O. guatemalae*, which some workers have been tempted to classify as a sub-species of *O. barbarus*. The consensus of opinion, however, is to place it on its own as a separate species.

The Vermiculated Screech Owl
(*Otus guatemalae*)

Despite its specific name of *guatemalae*, this species is found in Mexico and several areas of South America. Perhaps some taxonomist may yet absorb *O. barbarus* into the sub-species of the Vermiculated Screech Owl! After all, there are already ten other sub-species (see Table 12).

This is a small owl of about 20 cm (8 in), with a prominent yellow iris of the eye, giving it a fierce yet alert appearance. It is mainly dark grey above, but is vermiculated, with dusky wing-coverts spotted with white. The underparts vary from very light brown to white, but are densely, and sometimes quite coarsely, vermiculated with wavy brown bars plus just a few vertical streaks. In common with many owl species, we find a rufous phase in which the brown dorsal surface is replaced by chestnut and there is a large amount of rufous coloration on belly, chest and throat.

It can be distinguished from the Tropical Screech Owl by the lack of a distinct facial rim and the absence of a white superciliary (eye stripe). The Tropical Screech Owl also has heavy streaking on the underparts compared to the horizontal vermiculation of *O. guatemalae*. The calls are also different and diagnostic. That of the Vermiculated is described as a prolonged whinnying whistle on one pitch with no emphasis, while that of the slightly larger Tropical

Screech Owl is described as a purring trill terminating in a sharp querulous 'ook? oook?'.

The Vermiculated Screech Owl is not common among forest and regenerating woodland in lowlands and foothills. Its breeding habits have not been studied in detail but probably do not differ significantly from other species of *Otus* owls already described.

The West Peruvian or Roborate Screech Owl
(*Otus roboratus*)

This is a little known owl with no sub-species. It is found in north-west Peru.

The Pacific Screech Owl
(*Otus cooperi*)

This is a scrub-dwelling owl, found in central America and so far divided into two sub-species. The nominate sub-species, *Otus cooperi cooperi*, is found in El Salvador and north-west Costa Rica, while southern Mexico is the home of *Otus cooperi chiapensis*.

The Tropical or Choliba Screech Owl
(*Otus choliba*)

We have a great deal more information about this owl, although we still lack an in depth monograph on the species. As shown in Table 13, there are eight sub-species, stretching from Central to South America.

The species is about 22.5 cm (9 in) long and basically grey in colour with prominent ear tufts. These tufts are made of feathers and are not concerned with hearing, but are possibly used as a visual display during the breeding cycle. The iris of the eye is yellow and the facial area is a dirty white bordered by a black rim. The eye stripe is also white. The upper parts vary a little, from grey through to cinnamon-brown and are streaked and vermiculated with a rather darker brown. The wings are mottled and banded with cinnamon. The underparts are pale grey - white in some individuals. The bases of the feathers are a delicate shade of golden-buff with a sort of herring-bone pattern formed of dark bars and streaks. Occasionally a rufous phase occurs, the birds being obviously red above, while below there is a flush of cinnamon, although the markings are similar to the typical phase.

The species seems to be quite common and is the owl most frequently encountered on the Pacific slope, but its strictly nocturnal habits mean that unless the call is heard and actually recognised, this species tends to be under-recorded. It favours light second-growth woodland and its borders. Clearings and open areas with scattered trees also appear to be suitable and residential areas are occasionally accepted as breeding sites.

The Black-capped or Long-tufted Screech Owl
(*Otus atricapillus*)

This typical *Otus* owl is found in central and south-east Brazil. Although not well documented, we can assume that its future must be threatened by the wholesale destruction of the natural woodland of this country. Some authorities think that St Catherine's Screech Owl (*Otus sanctaecatherinae*) may be only a sub-species of *Otus atricapillus*. Apart from the fact that it is found in dry forests of Brazil, very little data is available.

The Rufescent Screech Owl
(*Otus ingens*)

This is another South American species which is found in the scrubland of the Andes, from Columbia to Bolivia. There are three sub-species. These are *Otus ingens ingens*, found in Ecuador, *Otus ingens colombianus*, from central Colombia, and *Otus ingens venezuelanus*, the population of which is centred on western Venezuela.

The Tawny-bellied Screech Owl
(*Otus watsonii*)

This owl occurs around the Amazon and Orinoco basins, there being only two sub-species, namely *Otus watsonii watsonii*, found in northern and upper areas of the Amazon, and *Otus watsonii usta*, found in central Brazil to northern Argentina.

The Puerto Rico Screech Owl
(*Otus nudipes*)

This has two sub-species, but little is known about either of them. *Otus nudipes nudipes* is confined to Puerto Rico itself, while *Otus nudipes newtoni* occurs on the islands of St Thomas, St John and St Croix.

The Bare-legged or Bare-shanked Screech Owl
(*Otus clarkii*)

This owl occurs in Costa Rica and Panama. There are no sub-species. The bird is almost 25 cm (10 in) in length. It is thus quite large as far as screech owls go and as its plumage is obviously spotted and ear tufts are present, is easy to recognise. The iris is yellow and thus also easy to spot, but in any case it is the only Screech Owl found in the mountain forests where it has been recorded as high as 2,132 metres (7,000 ft). It does not seem inclined to venture below 1,219 metres (4,000 ft). This in accessible habitat means that it may not be as rare as was once thought and the fact that it is mainly nocturnal also makes a census difficult, even although its high musical hooting in two equal parts — 'co, coo,coo,coo — is very diagnostic.

The facial area is tawny-cinnamon in colour and the upper surface is dark red-brown, mottled and streaked with black. There are white spots on the scapulars and wing-coverts. The undersurface is brown with black streaks and bars which contrast with dark brown bars and white spots. The belly becomes paler towards the vent. The bare tarsi, which account for the owl's vernacular name, are difficult to see in the field, but quite obvious on a museum skin. Little is known about their breeding, biology or behaviour.

The White-throated Screech Owl
(*Otus albogularis*)

This is another South American species which is distributed along the Andes from Venezuela to Ecuador. Four sub-species have so far been recognised: *Otus albogularis albogularis* occurs in Columbia and northern Ecuador, *Otus albogularis obscurus* in north-west Venezuela, *Otus albogularis meridensis* in western Venezuela, and there is an east Ecuador sub-species, *Otus albigularis acquatorialis*.

The Cloud-forest Screech Owl
(*Otus marshalli*)

This has no sub-species and is confined to south-east Peru, where there has, as yet, been no definitive study of the species.

The Least Screech Owl
(*Otus minimus*)

The same deficiency is also seen in the case of this owl from western Bolivia. The species is also sometimes called Carriker's Owl. There are no sub-species.

The White-faced Scops Owl
(*Otus leucotis*)

This owl occurs in South Africa where it is called the Witwanguil. It has been quite thoroughly studied, although there are still gaps in our knowledge. There are three sub-species: *Otus leucotis leucotis* occurs from Senegal to Ethiopia and Kenya, *Otus leucotis margarethae* is confined to the Sudan, and *Otus leucotis granti* occurs from southern Zaire and Tanzania to Cape Province.

It is quite large for an *Otus* owl, being between 25 and 28 cm (10-11 in), thus enabling the species to add small birds, mice and other small mammals to its main diet of insects. The dark ears set against a very pale face are a distinctive feature, reflected in its common name, while the white along the edge of the scapulars is also diagnostic. The adults have a number of black streaks on the crown, but these are lacking in young birds. The sexes are alike to look at, but the females tend to be marginally larger.

Ornithologists have been at pains to explain why female predators are often larger than their mates. One view is that she can thus defend her young against the possibility of the male eating them, but as he shows no inclination to do so, we can perhaps discount this. Another theory is that the two can thus take slightly different prey, avoiding competition when food is scarce.

One unusual feature of the behaviour of the White-faced Scops Owl is that it is thought to be able to construct a nest of its own, even though this is invariably flimsy. It does, however, prefer to take over an old nest, usually one built by hawks or corvids, which is large enough for the owl's purpose. The clutch usually contains only two or three, white, slightly glossy eggs, laid during August to November in Zimbabwe, but from July to February in south-west Africa and Natal. The average measurements of these eggs are 30 × 40 mm (1.2 × 1.6 in).

The incubation period is around 30 days. Worden

and Hall (1977) established that the male actually assists in the incubation for a short period during the night, while the female stretches her wings and perhaps gets a chance to feed. This is a most unusual event in the breeding biology of owls. The female, however, is in charge for the whole of the day. By all accounts she sits closely and, if disturbed, will defend her nest with great ferocity — or, as some of us would prefer to say, courage.

When hatched, the chicks are clothed in a grey-white fluffy down and their eyes open on the fourth day. The flight feathers develop rapidly from about the fourteenth day and after the twenty-first day they are exercising their wings on the ends of branches. They can fly tentatively from their fifth week. Should they fall from a branch before they can fly, they show a remarkable ability to climb back to the safety of the nest, using their long claws to grip with. They are able to breed in the year following birth and add their stuttering and stammering trills to the night chorus.

The call consists of a strong 'w-h-h-h-oo-oo' followed by a much weaker 'oo-oo' and thus the call is bisyllabic. The White-faced Owl also produces a low-pitched 'to-whit, to-wheet'.

The Sao Thomé Scops Owl
(*Otus hartlaubi*)

This owl is listed as rare among the birds of the Afro-tropical area, although it is fairly widespread in areas of forest. It is thought that heavy use of pesticides, plus competition from Barn Owls and predation by cats, have combined to reduce the population.

The Giant Scops Owl
(*Otus gurneyi*)

This owl is sometimes classified among the *Otus* species, but other taxonomists have placed it in a different genus and named it *Mimizuku gurneyi*. It is found in Marindugue and Mindanao, but little is known of its behaviour.

The Crested Owl
(*Lophostrix cristata*)

This species are found in Central and South America, from Mexico to Bolivia and Amazonian Brazil. Although related to the *Otus* owls, it is sufficiently different to warrant being placed in its own genus of *Lophostrix*. At 40 cm (16 in), it is a large owl, with very long ear tufts coloured buff to white. The colour of the iris of the eye varies from brown to yellow. The upper surface is sooty-brown, but attractively mottled with red. The pale eyestrip, which extends right across to the ear tufts, is a diagnostic feature. The wings are heavily spotted with white. The undersurface appears mottled due to a number of dark bands on the buff background colour of the plumage.

It is not a very common species and is found in forests or second-growth woodland as well as in humid lowland areas. It is apparently strictly nocturnal, feeding upon small mammals plus some birds and insects. The call is distinctive and low-pitched, reminding some people of the sound made by frogs. Other workers have likened it to the gobbling of a turkey. Three sub-species have been recognised: *Lophostrix cristata cristata* is found throughout the Guianas and north and west Brazil, *Lophostrix cristata stricklandi* occupies an area from southern Mexico to western Columbia, while *Lophostrix cristata wedeli* occurs in the eastern area of Panama.

The final two species to be described in this chapter also warrant the status of a different genus, although little information is available on either.

The Palau Scops Owl
(*Pyrroglaux podargina*)

This owl, found on Palau Island, is considered by some taxonomists to be an *Otus* owl and is thus also named *Otus podarginus*. Until a detailed study is available, it is difficult to assign it with confidence.

The Akun Scops Owl or Maned Owl
(*Jubula letti*)

This owl has also been named *Lophostrix letti*, but most workers now accept *Jubula*. It is distributed in the forested areas of West and Central Africa where it feeds mainly upon insects.

This chapter has considered a large number of mainly insect-eating small owls, the presence of which often goes undetected, so that they perhaps appear to be rarer than they really are. This certainly does not apply to the huge *Bubo* owls which are the subject of the next chapter.

Great Horned Owl   (*Bubo virginianus*)

CHAPTER SIX

The Bubo Owls

This magnificent genus of owls contains some of the world's most impressive avian predators which have been feared, respected and worshipped since the dawn of human times. Twelve species are accepted by most authorities.

The Great Horned Owl
(*Bubo virginianus*)

This mighty North American species has been 'split' into seventeen sub-species which are summarised in Table 14. The biology is, of course, basically similar throughout the range. The size varies between 45 and 63 cm (18-25 in). This is the only owl of such a size occurring in its range. It has ear tufts which do look rather like horns, hence the name. It cannot be confused with hawks of a similar size because it is darker in colour, has a larger head and its neck is hunched up so as to be invisible during flight.

The Great Horned Owl has adapted to a variety of habitats, ranging from large city parks, to farms and rocky canyons with no tree cover. In contrast to this, they also appear to be perfectly happy in dense woodland. They are most common, however, in wooded or rocky areas which provide them with the ideal combination of nest sites and food availability. This habitat would therefore seem to be its natural niche.

As one would expect with such an adaptable species, the choice of nest sites is also variable. A cavity on the ground or at heights up to 20 m (66 ft) both seem to be equally satisfactory, the cavity being utilised just as it is found, although occasionally a few feathers are added. Whether these have been moulted by the sitting females or plucked out deliberately is open to debate. Great Horned Owls have been known to use an abandoned squirrel's drey as a breeding site as well as the discarded nests of herons, hawks and corvids. Crevices in trees and cliffs, as well as rocky ledges, have also proved acceptable.

The clutch size is two to four almost spherical white eggs with a rough surface. The incubation period is around 30 days, but there have been reports of periods as short as 25 and as long as 35 days. Some confusion may have arisen here because incubation begins with the laying of the first egg, probably to ensure that the young hatch at intervals. In the event of adverse hunting conditions the stronger can then consume the weaker and ensure the survival of at least one owlet from the single brood produced each year. It could just be, however, that the clutch may be incubated from the appearance of the first egg to prevent the egg freezing, as the Great Horned Owl does occur in some pretty cool areas. Whatever the truth of the matter, both male and female appear to incubate, but the bulk of the sitting is done by the larger female, while the male provides most of the food.

When the young do hatch they are covered in a rather scanty coating of pale down and the parents need to brood them very closely indeed. Their eyes do not open for a week and they are unable to fly until they are around ten weeks old. Even then the owlets seem reluctant to break the bond with their parents, and continue to beg for food until driven away by them. They have to do this in order to prepare for the following year's breeding.

Great Horned Owls are fiercely monogamous and are extremely vocal in maintaining and strengthening the pair bond. The call is a haunting 'whoo-whoowhoo-whoo', with the male's voice being pitched appreciably lower than that of his mate. The breeding season often starts very early and the cold winter woodlands and canyons echo to their calls. This can be quite nerve-shattering to the human ear, but it also spells death to smaller birds and especially mammals, which make up the bulk of the diet. In Kansas eggs can be laid between mid-January and mid-March, with a peak reached during February. In Oklahoma eggs are even laid in early February and young have been reported early in March; the breeding season seems to be more protracted here, however, with eggs reported as being laid as late as early June. Texans will claim an even longer breeding period, with records of laying as early December and as late as July.

The Eagle Owl
(*Bubo bubo*)

This is the Old World equivalent of the North American Great Horned Owl and, as you would expect of such a widespread species, it has already been divided into 23 sub-species which are summarised in Table 15. *Bubo bubo bubo* is spread across Scandinavia and Western Europe as far as the west of the USSR, and it is to this sub-species that the following account applies, although the rest of the sub-species are unlikely to differ in general breeding habits and behaviour since, by the very fact that they are of the species, they would, if they actually met, be able to breed together. *Bubo bubo bubo* is often referred to as the north European race of the Eagle Owl. 'Race' and 'sub-species' are therefore synonymous.

This huge, and at times awe-inspiring species, provided me with a most unforgettable experience. While presenting a television programme I had to interview a handler of eagle owls and it so happened that he and I had to share a large cage with six birds. Because they knew him but not me, I was treated to several threat displays and one aggressive fly past during which a female delivered a smart blow to the back of my neck with her foot!

Although present in many European countries there is no doubt that the Eagle Owl is declining throughout its range and that in some areas this decline is serious enough to demand immediate attention.

This is Europe's largest owl, the female being larger than the male. It can vary in length from 66-71 cm (26-28 in) in length and has a mighty wing span of up to 1.8 m (6 ft). The Eagle Owl is clearly a formidable predator. It is hardly surprising, therefore, to find that it has been persecuted by people for centuries and that some countries, such as Norway, were once prepared to pay a bounty upon it. Between 1908 and 1915 a total of 1,359 of these splendid birds were officially shot.

The plumage is mainly brown, but apart from its size other unmistakable features are its brilliant orange eyes and prominent ear tufts, often over 5 cm (12 in) long. These owls are of a very sturdy build, females reaching 3.5 kg (7 ½ lb) in weight with the males averaging 0.5 kg (1 lb) less. The dorsal surfaces are dark brown, but mottled with an attractive pale orange. The wings and tail are obviously barred, while the ventral surface is a much paler bluff and streaked with a contrasting dark brown. The markings on the breast are broader than those on the abdomen. The legs and feet are covered in brown feathers and the claws are black.

The scientific classification of Eagle Owls is far from agreed upon and the Eagle Owl is sometimes grouped with the American Great Horned Owl (*Bubo virginianus*) and the South African Cape Eagle Owl (*Bubo capensis*) and considered as a single species. This was certainly the view expressed in 1973 by Eck and Busse who grouped all three under the heading *Bubo bubo*, which they divided into 43 sub-species. The modern view, however, is to consider the three as separate species based upon significant plumage differences. The reason for the apparent confusion is the fact that it is only very recently, in evolutionary terms, that the three species developed from a single ancestor, a process which is doubtless still continuing. The rest of this section will therefore concentrate upon *Bubo bubo* first, and then some consideration will be given to the Great Horned and Cape Eagle Owls.

Eagle Owls breed across much of continental Europe from Norway and Sweden south of latitude 69°N, south through USSR, central and south-east Europe as far as the German Rhineland and the French Alps but with some increasingly isolated populations in Italy, Sicily, the Balkans and even in Spain and Portugal where it is classified as a separate sub-species, *Bubo bubo hispanuss*.

As mentioned earlier, state-paid bounties in such countries as Norway have caused almost irreparable damage to the species and the French populations have still not recovered from a long period during which the Eagle Owl was classed as vermin under a ruling which was only relaxed in the 1970s. There seems to have been some recovery in West Germany where, as in Sweden, some inspired reintroduction schemes have proved successful. In Britain there is no native population but breeding programmes, particularly in the Norfolk Wildlife Park, have provided a stock of birds to be used in other countries' reintroduction schemes. Such schemes as this prevent in-breeding and thus strengthen the gene pool. It hardly seems possible that any wild Eagle Owls exist in Britain and yet terrified non-ornithologists have sometimes emerged from the depths of Scotland's pine woods telling stories of a huge owl with glowing orange eyes! Scientists must always be sceptical but should always also be prepared to leave room for a miracle!

The preferred habitat is stretches of open woodland, but with enough protective cover, near to mountainous areas up to the substantial height of 4,500 m (14,625 ft). Because of its wide distribution the Eagle Owl may be found from hot southern deserts to the cool belts of coniferous taiga forests. This also accounts for the division of the species into a large number of geographical sub-species, which keeps the classification of this and related species in an almost continual state of flux. It is such a solitary species, even during the breeding season, that it is notoriously difficult to census. The total European population probably does not exceed 7,000 pairs and, as such, the Eagle Owl should be regarded as the area's most vulnerable owl species. It requires maximum protection and studies of its future requirements if it is to survive.

The onset of the breeding season is signalled by an almost continual hooting, the sound being described as 'oophu-ooha-oohu', which dominates the courting areas during December and January. Indeed, the scientific name of *Bubo* derives directly from the Greek *Buzo*, meaning 'to hoot'. By late February or early March even in the coldest areas, nest sites have been selected and at this time a surprisingly varied vocabulary of noises is produced, including rattling, grating and especially moaning noises which can, to human ears, sound very disconcerting.

Although sites in hollow trees and the abandoned nests of raptors or corvids may be selected, the favourite position is on the ground among rocks overlooking river valleys. Apart from initial selection, no effort is made at serious nest building and the clutch of two to four white eggs are often laid on a protective mat of leaves. Fewer eggs seem to be laid in the north of the range than in the south, probably due to the better food supply in the latter regions. The eggs are not quite oval, an average size being 5 × 6 cm (2 × 2.4 in). These are incubated for about 35 days by the female alone, beginning with the laying of the second egg, and she is usually occupied by this task throughout April.

This is a period of intensive activity for the male who keeps up a supply of food which he usually delivers to a 'food station' from which his mate collects her meal. This may well be a safety precaution to avoid giving the position of the breeding site away, although there are records of delivery direct to the nest. The eggs seem to be laid at two-day intervals and the young therefore hatch according to this timetable. During the fledging period of around seven weeks, the male continues to stock the feeding station alone. Both sexes, however, actually feed the young.

Without having positive proof, it would seem that the survival rate of young Eagle Owls, after they leave their parents' care, is likely to be low as their power of flight takes a considerable time to develop fully. Some pairs, however, continue to look after their young during this vulnerable time. Many young owls are killed during this period through flying into electrical power lines or as victims of traffic accidents. Although females can breed at the end of their first year, they are known to be more successful as they get older perhaps because by then they, and their mates, have learned to tap the available food supply.

Because of its huge size, the diet of the Eagle Owl is very varied. Although it consists mainly of mammals, birds do form a significant portion of the diet — often as high as 45 per cent. A Swedish survey examined 484 prey items, including 18 per cent Brown Rat (*Rattus norvegicus*), with voles and other rodents making up another 18 per cent, and minor items including Hooded Crow (*Corvus corone*) 9 per cent, Hedgehog (*Erinaceous europaeus*) 8 per cent, Red Squirrel (*Sciurus vulgaris*) 7 per cent, Duck 5 per cent and Hares (*Lepus capensis* and *L. timidus*) 4 per cent. Reptiles and amphibians were also reported as being taken from time to time, as were a number of other owl species, including Tawny, Long-Eared, Tengmalm's, Little, Hawk, and even a Snowy Owl which must have constituted something of a battle. What better way, however, of reducing competition from other owls in the same habitat!

The Cape Eagle Owl
(*Bubo capensis*)

This is a most attractive species, measuring between 48 and 53 cm (19-21 in) and separated into three sub-species. These are the Ethiopian and Eritrean Eagle Owl (*Bubo capensis dillonii*), *Bubo capensis mackinderi* which ranges from Zimbabwe northwards to the Kenyan highlands, and the nominate race, *Bubo capensis capensis*, found in Natal and Cape Province. The following account relates to the latter sub-species.

Despite its size, the Cape Eagle Owl has proved to be so elusive that it has certainly been under-recorded, although there is no doubt that it is not common. It is essentially a bird of mountainous and forested country, both of which terrains make it difficult to census and especially to study. In Robert's *Birds of South Africa* (1978) it was reported to be 'somewhat diurnal, even attacking its prey in daylight. Data is urgently required.' Let us first see how the species can be identified and then examine what advances have been made in the decade since those words were written.

The Cape Eagle Owl is not easily distinguished from the Spotted Eagle Owl (page 51), but it is obviously more heavily blotched with contrasting brown and white on both the back and the chest. The barring on the abdomen of the Cape Eagle Owl is also much less obvious than that on the Spotted Eagle Owl. The Cape Eagle Owl also has much larger feet, and eyes which are more orange than yellow. The voices are also different, that of *Bubo capensis* being rendered as a high-pitched double 'whooo-whooo', with the first note much louder than the second. There is also a strident 'wak-wak' alarm note.

Some idea of how elusive the species is can be appreciated from the fact that the first record of the bird in Zimbabwe (then Rhodesia) was a specimen collected by Barker in the Inyanga highlands in 1967. In July 1968 Peter Steyn discovered the first nest in a cave at Shangani. The same worker filled in many gaps for us when he wrote, in 1984:

'It was only in the decade after the discovery of the first Rhodesian Cape Eagle Owls that anything worthwhile was published on the species. Two leading ornithologists, Con Benson and Michael Irwin, wrote an important paper in the systematics and distribution of the species in Africa, in which they included the first two Rhodesian

records. This was complemented in 1972 by the excellent account of the biology of the species in Kenya by P. H. B. Sessions, a farmer, who provided yet another example of the value of amateur contributions in Rhodesia and gave an analysis of prey found in a cave in the Matopos. Then in 1976 Val Gargett, best known for her work on Black Eagles in the Matopos, gave a brief summary of breeding pairs found there (a more comprehensive account was published subsequently). This was followed in the same year by her paper in conjuction with Hans Grobler on the food of the Cape Eagle Owl in the Matopos. In 1977 the decade following the discovery of the species in Rhodesia was rounded off by my own account, in conjuction with Dave Tredgold, of the breeding biology studied at a nest at Shangani. Thus in the short space of ten years the biology of the Cape Eagle Owl advanced from the virtually unknown to the well known. Subsequently more has been found out, particularly in South Africa, where the species had hardly been studied.'

To me this is the most optimistic section in the whole of this book because it shows just what can be done if the will is there. We must hope that similar enthusiasts are working, or will begin to work, on other species and will provide the facts upon which future conservation polices can be accurately based.

Throughout the courtship procedure the pair become much more vocal and during long sessions of hooting the male expands a patch of white throat feathering, which is thought to be an effective visual signal at times of low light intensity when owls, of course, are at their most active. The nest site is always well concealed and may be on the ground providing there is enough cover to hide the nest scrapes. Ideally, however, they choose a ledge on a rocky face with either a sheer drop to protect it or an overhanging bush to screen the site. What has not been proved so far is that, as stated in some old textbooks, the nests of other species, such as corvids or diurnal birds of prey, are taken over. What is true is that a successful site will be used each year and only deserted if, for some reason, the breeding cycle fails.

The usual clutch is two eggs, although three are occasionally produced. They are white with an average measurement of 46 × 58 mm (1.8 × 2.3 in). In Kenya Sessions calculated the incubation period to be 36 days, which does not differ significantly from the 34-day period calculated by Steyn. The laying period would seem to be between June and December, depending upon the range being studied. The female certainly carries out the incubation, but workers have not found any food items near the nest until the young are being fed; it seems that she may therefore leave the nest to feed and it is speculated, although not yet proved, that the male may cover the eggs while she is away.

The eyes of the downy chicks are closed for at least a week following hatching. Between two and three weeks old, the eyes seem to be fully open and the feathers are well grown but still bristly and not yet ready to replace the greyish down. Between four and five weeks the grey down shows a visible barring and the white throat patch is already apparent. The young are brought food at this time by both parents but at this stage all they have to do is drop it close to the hungry chicks which swallow it greedily. By the time they are seven weeks old, the colour of the owlets' eyes has changed from yellow to a glowing orange and their wings are feathered in preparation for their maiden flight, probably made at the age of about 60 days.

The survival of any species will depend upon two needs being met. Successful breeding is essential for the long-term survival of the species, but feeding is vital to the short-term survival of the individual. Once more recent work in the field, by Gargett, Grobler and Steyn, has established that among the prey items are an assortment of mammals including hares, shrews and rodents. Birds recorded as being carried to the nest and/or incorporated into the pellets include the Red-winged Starling (*Onychognathum morio*), the Speckled Pigeon (*Columba guinea*) and even a juvenile Lanner Falcon (*Falco biarmicus*). All workers admit that there are still more facts awaiting discovery and we must hope that the next decade will be as fruitful as the last.

The Spotted Eagle Owl
(*Bubo africanus*)

This is the commonest large owl in southern Africa, being found in open grassland as well as in the bush and on hills. It has a habit of perching on roadside telegraph poles or fence posts from where it begins to hunt at dusk. At this time the 'ears' are thought to break up the outline of the bird and make it difficult to see. This is yet another possible function of ear tufts. Another theory is that the ears mimic the head pattern of large mammals and make them think twice before attacking a roosting owl in case it is a member of their own species. By the time they realise their mistake the owl may well have escaped.

There are three sub-species: the nominate race *Bubo africanus africanus*, which occurs from southern Africa north to Angola and Uganda, *Bubo africanus cinerascens*, present from French Guinea to Somalia, and *Bubo africanus milesi*, which is restricted to southern Saudi Arabia. In Spotted Eagle Owls the sexes are alike and are much greyer and more delicately banded on the undersurface than the Cape Eagle Owl (page 50). The iris of the eyes is yellow to orange and the bill and legs are both black. When the 'ears' are up and the eyes are glowing against the grey plumage, the appearance is quite daunting. On the upper surface there are a few randomly distributed white spots but they are not so numerous as to be striking enough to make the name accurate.

Spotted Eagle Owls pair for life, although either sex is quick to find another partner on the death of the first. The pair bond is strengthened by an increasing 'volley of hoots' as the breeding season approaches. The male's deeper 'hoo-hoo' is answered by the female's 'hoo-hoo-hoo', with the middle syllable of higher pitch to produce a surprisingly musical cadence. The preferred nest site is on the ground but trees and buildings are also chosen at times. The clutch of two to four eggs is laid between August and October and are incubated for 30 and 32 days. The female takes most of the responsibility for the incubation, sitting throughout the day and for most of the night, but she does take a few breaks through the night during which she may be fed by the male or do a little hunting on her own behalf.

Throughout the incubation period, and for the six-week fledging period, the male provides most of the food. The parents continue to feed the young for about one month after they can fly, the owlets finally becoming independent at around four months old. They are ready to breed the following year.

The diet consists mainly of small mammals and birds, but the Spotted Eagle is such an efficient killer that it can take suprisingly large prey including hornbills, pigeons, francolins and sandgrouse and there are also records of a Lanner Falcon (*Falco biarmicus*) and a Black-shouldered Kite (*Elanus caerulens*) being eaten.

Fraser's Eagle Owl or Nduk Eagle Owl
(*Bubo poensis*)

This African species is separated into two sub-species, *Bubo poensis poensis,* found from Ghana to northern Zaire, and *Bubo poensis vasseleri,* which is the race from northern Tanzania. Little is known of their habits and even their classification is the subject of disagreement, some taxonomists giving the Tanzanian race a specific rank of its own and naming it *Bubo vosseleri.* Under this name this owl is listed among the rarest birds in the world, its vernacular name being the Usambara Eagle Owl. It is described as a large, forest-dwelling owl with a population of between 200 and 800 individuals, which is centred in the forests of north-east Tanzania among the Usambara mountains. The area's natural vegetation has suffered badly from clearances to provide land to grow tea and cardamon, the latter being a spice used in Indian and Chinese cooking.

Cardamon is usually grown beneath an existing forest canopy and so may be less harmful to the owls' habitat than tea plantations. What is obviously needed, however, is a detailed study of the owls' feeding and breeding requirements, to see if a compromise with the needs of the indigenous human population is possible.

The Forest Eagle Owl
(*Bubo nipalensis*)

This is a species from the Indian sub-continent. There are two sub-species; *Bubo nipalensis nipalensis* occurs from the Himalayas to central Burma and India, while *Bupa nipalensis blighi* is found in Sri Lanka and is often called by its old name of the Ceylon Forest Owl. The description which follows refers to *Bubo nipalensis nipalensis,* but the Sri Lankan race is very similar.

It is a large species, around 63 cm (25 in) in length, and is bold and powerful enough to overpower species as large as the Common Peafowl (*Pavo cristatus*) and the Jungle Fowl (*Gallus gallus*) which is the ancestor of our domestic hen. Both these species are pounced upon and overpowered as they roost for the night in bamboo groves.

The Forest Eagle Owl is recognised by its pair of black-and-white ear 'horns' and also by its fully feathered legs and brown eyes, distinguishing it from the Great Horned Owl which has orange eyes. The upper surface is dark brown scalloped with buff, while the lower surface is pale buff, but with blackish bars on the throat and breast, and dark spots — almost chevron-shaped —on the belly. Salim Ali (1982) describes the vocabulary of the species as consisting of:

'A low, deep and far-sounding moaning hoot (Jordan). A long drawn kite-like whistle occasionally heard in the forest at night, has circumstantially been applied to this owl, likewise the diabolical blood-curdling shrieks of a woman being strangled, which have suggested the name "Devil Bird".

Here once more we have the association between the owl, the night and the supernatural; Salim Ali thinks that the mating call of the Sri Lankan race is the authentic devil bird (so called because of its association with the dark and its chilling call), but who knows?

This is certainly a tough species, living in the Himalayan foothills up to a height of 2,000 m (6,500 ft), although they seem to thrive best at about half this altitude, especially in damp deciduous or evergreen areas. The nominate race also occurs in Thailand, and the Laos central areas of Vietnam. Game birds, as we have seen, are its favourite prey items, but it has been reported fishing and killing lizards and snakes, and there are also reports of the Forest Eagle Owl attacking young deer and even a jackal!

The breeding season in the Himalayan region begins in February or March; in Kerda the season begins a month or two earlier, while the Sri Lankan race may not breed until May. The single smooth white egg measures, on average 50 × 61 mm (2 × 2.4 in) and is laid on the ground in a cave, on a sheltered ledge or perhaps in a hollow tree or an old nest. Complete data regarding incubation period, the relative role of the sexes, fledging period and dispersal behaviour are still to be recorded.

The Barred Eagle Owl or Malay Eagle Owl
(*Bubo sumatrana*)

This owl is of a similar size to *B. nipalensis* and is a major nocturnal predator in the mountainous rain forests of south-east Asia, Java, Bali and Borneo. Little or nothing is known of its breeding biology but, despite the lack of data, the study of museum skins has allowed the species to be split into two sub-species. These are *Bubo sumatrana sumatrana*, restricted to southern Burma, Malaysia and Sumatra, while the race found in Java, Bali and Borneo is named *Bubo sumatrana strepitans*.

Shelley's or the Banded Eagle Owl
(*Bubo shelleyi*)

This owl is found very rarely between Liberia and the southern Cameroon. There are no sub-species, which is not surprising because only four individuals have so far been described.

Verreaux's Giant Eagle, or the Milky Eagle Owl
(*Bubo lacteus*)

There can be no mistaking this formidable creature which is between 58 and 65 cm (23-25½ in) long, with a wing span of up to 155 cm (5 ft) and a weight of 3kg (6 ½ lb). It is tropical Africa's largest owl and is widely distributed south of the Sahara except in the still heavily forested Congo Basin — it prefers savanna woodland and riversides dominated by acacia. The vernacular name of 'milky', which is also part of the scientific name (*lacteus*) is somewhat confusing but almost certainly relates to its overall pale grey coloration, which is covered on both the dorsal and ventral surfaces by darker vermiculations. The ear tufts are rather stubby and beneath these the pale face stands out clearly, outlined in black. On each side of the bluish bill are black bristles. The huge dark brown eyes would be impressive enough on their own, but the pink eyelids cause those watching them for the first time to gasp in sheer surprise.

The prey is varied, as you would expect in a bird with such huge feet, but the work of Peter Steyn suggests a distinct preference for hedgehogs which are first killed and then literally turned inside out, the peeled skins being left to litter the area. The same worker also suggests that owls may perch by roads or tracks and then pick off mammals which cross them. Other species taken include hares and birds up to the size of guinea-fowls (around 60 cm/23 ½ in). They are considered a menace to any fowls which roost in the open.

In early stages of the breeding cycle the pair sit quite close together and jerk their bodies and flick their wings in unison. One wonders if those pink eyelids might not come in useful here! The male calls 'uh-uhu-oh-uh' and this elicits a lower pitched 'uh-uh' from the female. When the time comes to select a nest site there seems to be a preference for the old nests of other species, with preferred heights being in excess of 10 m (32 ½ ft). In the case of the Giant Eagle Owl, size, not possession, seems to be nine points of the law and there are records of Homerkop (*Scopus umbretta*) being evicted by this owl, and an even more bizarre record of an Egyptian Goose (*Alopochen aegyptiacus*) incubating a clutch of eggs inside a Hamerkop's nest with a Giant Eagle Owl incubating on top of the same large twiggy site! There are also records of owls' nests on top of the tangled communal nest of the Sociable Weaver (*Philetairus socius*).

Roberts reports *Bubo lacteus* as producing eggs between June and September, but Steyn suggests April to August with a peak between June and August; normally a period of dry cool weather which allows the owlet to fledge prior to the onset of the summer rains.

The two white, rough and pitted eggs average 51 × 63 mm (2 × 2 ½ in), but there are some suggestions that the second egg may be considerably smaller than the first. There is also some discrepancy with regard to the incubation period. Roberts states firmly that it is 25 days, but more recent studies have pushed this up, first to 33 days and then to 38 or 39 days. Obviously there is an urgent need for a series of definitive studies. It would seem to be fairly certain that the female does the majority, and almost certainly all, of the incubation duty, with the male only functioning as a waiter.

The nest of this species is more exposed than that of many owls and the incubating female is often exposed to the full glare of the sun — a most unusual experience for an owl. I have had many a chuckle at Peter Steyn's tongue-in-check idea that 'Reports of Giant Eagle Owls with brick-red eyelids may be the result of sunburn and are of no taxonomic significance!'

When it is hatched the chick is only sparsely covered with pale down, and by the end of the first week the pink eyelids are already recognisable. Thicker grey down is apparent in the third week and the future flight and contour feathers are already visible. The black face markings only appear in the fourth week and this is a useful guideline in estimating the owlet's age. When the chick leaves the nest at six weeks it still has traces of down, especially on the head, and bears a distinct resemblance to one of 'The Three Stooges' of Hollywood movies. The parents continue to provide food for a further month or so before 'insisting' that the owlet fends for itself. Readers will notice that I have suddenly switched from a discussion of a pair of owlets to a single chick. There is a sad reason for this. The two eggs are laid several days apart and one youngster is therefore much more powerful than the other and demands the bulk of the food. Whether the weaker sibling dies or is killed, the end result is the same — stronger eats weaker.

The Dusky Eagle or Horned Owl
(*Bubo coromandus*)

This large owl is found on the Indian subcontinent and in south-east Asia. It is about 58 cm (23 in) long and is separated into two sub-species. *Bubo coromandus klossii* occurs in southern Burma and Malaysia, while *Bubo coromandus coromandus* is widely distributed in damp woodland areas throughout the subcontinent south of the Himalayas, through northern India and east Pakistan and southwards to Mysore and Nilgiris. Once established, a pair seems to be faithful not only to each other, but also to the same breeding site.

The sexes are alike in appearance, with prominent ear tufts which are said to stick up like 'twin spires'. The overall colour of the plumage is grey-brown, finely mottled and vermiculated with white, especially the underparts. The shoulders are typified by a varying number of buff or white spots. The wing and tail feathers are light brown with paler cross bands and tips. The pale yellow eyes are particularly striking, especially when staring out from undergrowth at dusk.

Although it shuns broad daylight, this species may often be seen hunting for food an hour before sunset. Its call is a 'deep resonant, hollow "Wo Wo, Wo, wo-o-o-o", reminiscent of a large ping pong ball dropped from a height and allowed to bounce itself to silence, the sound getting fainter with each successive bounce' (*Salim Ali*). We have already seen this apt description recorded by Salim Ali for the Screech Owl (*Otus asio*), but the call of the Dusky Eagle Owl is of a lower pitch and, in any case, the two are geographically separated. This call is heard by day and night and is said to be more frequent during the cold wet season — it may be that the pair are courting at this time in preparation for producing young during a more gentle climatic period when they are more likely to survive.

The breeding season stretches from November to April, depending upon the area; in northern India the season peaks in December and begins later as one moves southwards. Nests of other large species are usually taken over, some surprisingly close to human habitation — it does, however, take an above average helping of courage, or perhaps foolhardiness, to disturb an incubating Eagle Owl! Salim Ali records that green leaves are occasionally used to line the nest. He also points out that trees standing in water are particularly favoured as nest sites and this may account for the appearance of water beetles in the diet which also includes hares, rats, squirrels, herons, lapwings, rollers, doves, parrots and corvids. The larger prey items seem to be decapitated before being taken to the nest, but the adults doubtless follow the owl tradition of swallowing their food whole.

The clutch size is invariably two — occasionally one — white eggs measuring 48 × 60 mm (1.9 × 2.4 in) are laid at intervals of several days, sometimes in excess of a week. As seen in the South African Giant Eagle Owl, this results in one chick being much larger than the other, and it is rare for both to survive. Little is known of the incubation and fledging period and again a long and thorough research project is needed to sort out the fine details of one of India's most beautiful birds.

The Akun Eagle Owl
(*Bubo leucostictus*)

This owl, from West and Central Africa is thought to take a large proportion of insects. There are no sub-species but this is not surprising since it is not at all well known.

The Philippine Eagle Owl
(*Bubo philippensis*)

This owl is probably restricted to the mountainous rain forest areas of the Philippines. Its biology and field characteristics are little known, and it is among the rarest birds in the world. What is needed for this species is a description similar to that produced for the Seychelles Scops Owl by Jeff Watson. There has been a movement in recent years to place the species in its own genus and call it *Pseudoptynx philippensis*. Two sub-species are recognised, namely *Pseudoptynx philippensis philippensis*, found on the islands of Luzon and Cebu, while *Pseudoptynx philippensis mindanensis* is restricted, it would appear, to Mindanao Island.

Eagle Owl   (*Bubo bubo*)   *aggressive display*

CHAPTER SEVEN

The Snowy Owl
(*Nyctea scandiaca*)

When a pair of these attractive white owls produced a clutch of eggs amid the rough landscape of the Shetland island of Fetlar in 1967, it was quite correctly regarded as one of the most exciting events in British ornithological history. Unfortunately, breeding has not occured since 1975 due, it is thought to the absence of a male for the only two females. The life span of the species is probably less then ten years and unless a male appears very soon, the Fetlar Snowy Owls will become extinct. The interest in the Shetland birds was intensified because of the fact that the species is nowhere common and there is reliable scientific evidence that it is actually declining in some areas.

Its range includes parts of north Asia and north Canada included in Holarctic region, a term invented to cover the combined Nearctic and Palaearctic zoogeographical regions. The Nearctic region includes North America, while the Palaearctic includes Europe, Asia north of the Himalayas and Africa north of the Sahara. The transitional area between Nearctic and Palaearctic includes Iceland, Greenland and Alaska — typical Snowy Owl habitat — and it is therefore right that we should classify it as a Holarctic species.

In view of the British record, it is interesting to read Salim Ali's account of its appearance in Pakistan:

'A specimen once taken (March 3 c1876) at Mardan in W. Pakistan (c34°14'N, 72°5'E) and several other examples claimed to have been seen . . . at the same time. Evidently an accidental waif during an "exodus year" when the species, owing to food scarcity cycles irrupts enormous distances south of its normal range. No subsequent record . . . A powerful diurnal owl with a buzzard-like flight, sometimes chasing birds and striking them down in the air like a falcon. Lives largely on rodents and other small mammals.'

There are no sub-species of this, one of the largest owl species in the world, which has a wingspan of around 1.5 m (5 ft). Its body length is between 53 and 66 cm (21-26 in) and it is a most formidable predator. These birds have a very pronounced rounded head. The females are larger than the males and, unlike the situation in most owls, there is a pronounced sexual dimorphism (i.e. the sexes can be told apart by appearance). The adult male is almost pure white, except for a small but varying number of brown spots and bars. The female, by contrast, has white background plumage prominently marked by dark brown bars across the breast, dorsal surface and the wings. It would seem that these markings are much less obvious in winter, due to the fact that the dark patterns are scuffed off by contact with ice or rough vegetation. The normal pattern appears again following the next moult. An unusual feature of the species is an extra moult during the summer.

Several questions arise regarding the value of these colour patterns. Why do the sexes differ in colour? Why does white predominate? When finding food becomes difficult during winter, camouflage is vital to hunting success. The fact that the sexes have different colour patterns means that they will be more successful in areas which suit this patterning and this will serve to disperse the Snowy Owl over a wider and therefore more varied hunting terrain. Perhaps even more important in this respect is the difference in size, which enables the female to take larger prey than her mate. It is perhaps during the breeding season that the female's barred plumage comes into its own, enabling the sitting bird to blend perfectly into the tundra-type vegetation, especially when thrown into shadow by the low Arctic sun.

The white of the plumage itself means that less body heat is lost by radiation; a vital factor to a bird struggling to survive in freezing conditions. A further essential adaptation is seen in the legs, which are feathered down to the toes. This, apart from the obvious insulation provided, prevents moisture, picked up when ice melts during the day, from freezing during the cold night. Left clinging to the skin, this ice could greatly reduce the body temperature. There are also air spaces between the cells of the feathers, which add significantly to their insulation efficiency. Both sexes have tiny ear tufts which are not easily visible and the feathering making up the facial disc is not as complete as in many other owls. The eyes are bright yellow, while the bill and powerful claws are dark brown.

Females, being larger, are obviously heavier than their mates, the corresponding statistics being 2,250 and 1,750 gm (79 and 62 oz), respectively.

One other unusual feature of the species should be mentioned, namely the presence of the recognisable first-year plumage. The barring is much heavier than that of the female. It is possible, even at this age, to distinguish the sexes. The barring on the young males is much less clearly defined and much browner than that of the young females, which is almost black, the barring on the ventral surface being crossed, while the bars on the dorsal surface are U- or even V-shaped. The lower nape is so devoid of barring that it gives the appearance of a white collar. The face is also almost white, as is the breast, while the top of the head is spotted with dark brown. The whole effect is to render the plumage of the first-year female Snowy Owl as the one most easily recognised.

The distribution is distinctly circumpolar, concentrated between 58°N and 13°N, embracing the extreme north of both America and Eurasia, plus north-east Greenland and Iceland. Their habitat preference is for open and often windswept tundra, but they do require a few prominent rocks or outcrops which can be used as essential observation posts. Another essential requirement is an adequate food supply which, over most of the range, is mainly the Brown Lemming (*Lemnus sibiricus*), a small rodent whose population fluctuates widely over a four-year cycle. The population of the Snowy Owl itself reflects this, the breeding cycle depending entirely upon the lemming. Indeed, in years of lemming shortage the owls may not even attempt to breed.

In winters during lemming shortages the owls may travel considerable distances to the south and this is when European birdwatchers, as far south as Britain, enjoy the sight of Europe's second largest owl (its impressive dimensions being exceeded only by those of the Eagle Owl).

These trends, which are so dependent upon the status of the lemming, make the Snowy Owl populations a tricky proposition for scientists to calculate. Even in Iceland it is decidedly rare; in Finland there has been a significant decline since 1930, while the 'small' breeding populations reported from the USSR, Norway and Sweden would also seem to be declining. Although the long-term reasons for this are not yet known, the pressure has been taken off the species over much of Western Europe by laws prohibiting shooting and even photography in areas where it is particularly vulnerable.

In North America the pattern is even more pronounced, with occasional spectacular irruptions reaching the United States from the normal range up in the Arctic regions of Canada. The most impressive of these irruptions took place during the winter of 1926-27 when almost 2,500 sightings occurred, with the odd straggler reaching as far south as California and Bermuda.

For most of the year the Snowy Owl is usually silent, but as the breeding season approaches the male produces a harsh barking sound which, in 1968, Tulloch described as 'ergh-ergh-ergh-ergh', the female responding with a higher-pitched 'eergh-eergh-eergh'. This is, however, a difficult species to observe and there also seems to be some degree of individual variation, so we need to wait for further observations before firming up our opinions on Snowy Owl language.

The nest site is chosen during courtship, usually being sited on a raised area containing a suitable depression which is used without any lining. The pure white eggs vary in number from four to ten, the clutch size apparently depending upon the availability of lemmings or other food. The clutch is usually completed between April and June and is incubated by the female alone. She begins with the first egg. Each takes

Snowy Owl   *(Nyctea scandiaca)*

around 33 days to hatch and thus a nest of young may show a great variation in size. In the event of a failure in food supply, there is no doubt that the stronger chicks eat the weaker.

The male does not desert his mate, but provides a regular food supply as well as defending the nest site with great noise and courage against predators, including human intruders. Both sexes employ an effective distraction display, during which they feign injury and draw predators away from the vulnerable young. The Gyr Falcon (*Falco rusticolus*) and Peregrine Falcon (*Falco peregrinus*) have both been known to take Snowy Owlets, as has the Arctic Fox (*Alopex lagopus*).

Both parents feed the young and for the first ten days of the fledgelings' life they show a surprising degree of tenderness, the female accepting food from the male and tearing it into fleshy, easily digested lumps for the young. From the tenth day onwards the prey is delivered and swallowed whole, the young at this stage being able to handle the bones and produce pellets. The chicks are fully fledged at around two months and, so long as the lemming population holds up, they soon become efficient hunters. They are usually capable of breeding in the following year.

While the lemming is the staple diet, other organisms are also taken, especially when the owls are out of their usual range. In Shetland the Rabbit (*Oryctolagus cuniculus*) assumes a vital importance, but birds are also taken, including the Oystercatcher (*Haematopus ostralegus*), the Lapwing (*Vanellus vanellus*) and other members of the wader and grouse families. Amphibians and fish are also taken, the latter obtained by plunge-diving following a hover over the water (in the manner of an Osprey (*Pandion haliaetus*).

Snowy Owl *(Nyctea scandiaca) alighting by the side of her nest*

It has been pointed out that the diet of the Snowy Owl is not suited to the warmer areas of Western Europe and that providing the supply of arctic mammals is sufficient, they are quite able to survive the Arctic cold in which they have evolved, despite the very low temperatures. Gessaman (1972) investigated food and oxygen consumption and the carbon dioxide production of four female Snowy Owls exposed to different temperatures and air speeds, which enabled him to calculate the chill factor to which they were subjected. He found that the standard metabolic rate was only 42 per cent of the value expected and the thermal conduction was lower than figures calculated for any other bird and similar to that of the Arctic Fox. Here, then, is a perfectly adapted Arctic owl, with no competitor to challenge it within its chosen habitat.

CHAPTER EIGHT

The Fish Owls

This collection of seven specialist feeders is included in the sub-family Buboninae and is divided into two genera — *Ketupa* and *Scotopelia*.

Blackiston's Fish Owl
(*Ketupa blackistoni*)

This species comes from north-east Asia, and has not been fully investigated. We do know, however, that it nests on the ground, feeds mainly on crayfish and is around 60 cm (23 ½ in) in length. Four sub-species are recognised. *Ketupa blackistoni blackistoni* is found on the island of Hokkaido, *Ketupa blackistoni piscivorous* occurs through western Manchuria, *Ketupa blackistoni doerriesi* is found through north-east Asia, and *Ketupa blackistoni karafustonis* is the race found on Sakhalin Island. There has been a move in recent years to combine Blackiston's and the Brown Fish Owl (*Ketupa zeylonensis*) together to form what is termed a 'super-species' but I do believe that the consensus of opinion is to keep them separate. Blackiston's is likely to remain rare because it is dependent upon fast flowing water which must remain open throughout the year. In freezing conditions populations can become greatly reduced.

The Brown Fish Owl
(*Ketupa zeylonensis*)

This bird is much more thoroughly documented and yet there are still many gaps in our knowledge. It is another large owl, 56 cm (22 in) long, with a wingspan of 178 cm (70 in). Some workers have suggested that females are about the same size as the males but with a greater wingspan, but it seems to me that these measurements are as yet based upon a small amount of data. Such a large owl is bound to be confused with the Eagle Owl. There are, however, three fundamental differences between the two species. First, in the air the Fish Owl sounds quite noisy since it lacks the soft plumage and feather adaptations essential for silent flight: a bird which specialises in catching fish, silent flight would have no evolutionary advantage. Second, the facial disc is not particularly well developed and again this is predictable as the facial disc is designed to focus sound during the hunting of mammalian or avian prey and is not at all relevant to fishing. The third point of contrast to the Eagle Owl also relates to the hunting technique. The feet of Fish Owls are not feathered, but are provided with sharp protrusions on the soles to enable slippery struggling fish to be lifted from the water. The claws are also curved to suit this purpose.

Although fish make up most of their diet, this owl will also take carrion — Burton (1973) reported one feeding on a dead crocodile — as well as insects, crabs, amphibians, reptiles and birds up to the size of the pheasant family (55-95 cm/22-36 in), as well as a varied assortment of mammals.

Always found near water, the Brown Fish Owl is nocturnal and extremely territorial. Because it is so nocturnal it needs also to be extremely vocal. Salim Ali described the call as a deep 'hollow sounding "boom-boom" or "boom-o-boom", with a peculiar rever-berating ventriloquistic quality repeated at intervals.

Suddenly "exploding" in the stillness of the forest, the call has a distinctly eerie effect'. Many owl watchers have remarked on nocturnal duets which continue for long periods and in 1970 Etchécopar and Hue described the species as producing a mewing sound which reminded them of the call of the Stone Curlew (*Burhinus oedienemus*).

Salim Ali's description applies to the Indian race, but it appears similar in all the sub-species, of which there are four. *Ketupa zeylonensis zeylonensis* is the Sri Lankan race, while *Ketupa zeylonensis semenowi* occurs from Israel (Golan Heights) to north-west India; *Ketupa zeylonensis leschenault* is found in India, Burma and Thailand, and *Ketupa zeylonensis orientalis* is the race found from north-east Burma to south-east China and Indochina.

A variety of nest sites is chosen, many close to human habitation. Old abandoned nests of diurnal birds of prey and corvids are frequently used, as are holes in riverbanks, hollow trees, buildings and crevices in rock faces. The information on the breeding biology is rather sketchy and a thorough monograph is sadly lacking.

The breeding season is between November and May. There is some evidence that the nest may be lined with leaves and perhaps feathers. The clutch size is either one or two, with very occasionally three, slightly glossy white eggs, measuring on average 50 × 60 mm (2 × 2.4 in). Incubation takes about five weeks and it is thought, but not proved, that the male may assist in incubation.

No reliable details are yet available on the fledging times or behaviour, but it should be stressed that this information is urgently needed because there is a marked decline of the Brown Fish Owl in some parts of its range. There are, for example, no recent records for Turkey and the population around the Golan Heights is now down to below ten pairs — a desperate situation. This owl formerly bred in Galilee but completely vanished from the area following the indiscriminate use of thallium sulphate to kill rodents in the 1950's.

We surely do not need a *reason* to preserve any living species, but if we had to find a good reason for this magnificent bird to exist then it would surely be its graceful hunting manoeuvres, even though its flight is not silent. It approaches a stretch of water, often illuminated by ghostly moonlight, and sweeps over the surface, suddenly lowering its feet like an aircraft's undercarriage and plunging its talons into a fish. There is no more magnificent sight.

The Tawny Fish Owl
(*Ketupa flavipes*)

This owl is found alongside streams running through forests from Kashmir to southern China and in south-east Asia and Taiwan. There are no sub-species. It is around 61 cm (24 in) long, with an upper plumage of rich tawny with buff on the scapulars and wing coverts. Both the wing and tail quills are dark brown, almost black, contrasting sharply against the buff bars and tips. The undersurface is an attractive russet colour with dark brown stripes on the feather shafts. Another identifiable feature of the species is in the form of a white throat patch.

This species is crepuscular (hunting at dawn and dusk) but also partially diurnal. This is logical because hunting for fish is a visual skill with no real need for a sense of hearing. The normal hunting technique is to perch on a tree overlooking water, before plunging down to grab fish, crabs, amphibians and reptiles, as well as a good number of game birds of the size of a jungle fowl and pheasants. The dependence upon fish, however, is great, as the species struggles to feed properly when the water is frozen.

When it comes to the breeding biology, little is yet known. The voice has not been recorded very often but is reported by Salim Ali and Ripley to be a deep 'whoo-hoo', although Baker has noted a cat-like mewing call. Breeding seems to be between December and early March, with a clutch of two white eggs, each averaging 47 × 57 mm (1.85 × 2.2 in). The site is often quite high up in trees, in the old nest of a Fish Eagle. There are records of holes in riverbanks or crevices in ravines being chosen, but it is a brave researcher who approaches the nest too closely, as the female in particular is said to be fierce in defence of her offspring. It is probably, but not certainly established, that the female does most of the incubation. Neither the length of the incubation nor the fledging period has been established with any certainty.

The Malay or Buffy Fish Owl
(*Ketupa ketupa*)

This is a similar species to *K. flavipes*, but one about which we know surprisingly little. It seems to be a little

Rufous Fishing Owl *(Scotopelia ussheri)*

Vermiculated Fishing Owl (*Scotopelia bouvieri*)

greyer in plumage than other Fish Owls and to frequent forest streams in south-east Asia and associated islands eastwards to Borneo. Its diet is predominantly fish and the single white egg is often laid in a hole in a tree. Accurate details of voice and breeding biology are not available.

Pel's Fishing Owl
(*Scotopelia peli*)

This owl measures around 64 cm (25 in) and is distinguished by its reddish-brown colour plus the fact that it has bare legs, no clearly denoted facial disc and no 'horns'. The last three features are all related to its habit of feeding on fish (see the Brown Fish Owl, page 61). Roberts reports that males, on average, tend to be smaller than their mates.

South Africa has three species of Fish Owl, this species being the most widespread, although quite rare in the east of Cape Province, spreading northwards to Ethiopia and westwards into the Congo basin. It is most frequently found in the Okovango delta. No reliable study of the species was made until Liversedge published his observations in 1976. He confirmed that the female was larger than her mate, to such an extent that he could distinguish between the pair as they roosted together in trees.

He also found himself at odds with reports that mammals and insects formed part of the prey — he discovered a total dependence upon fish and reported that even captive birds refused mammalian food whenever it was offered. The fish species preferred seemed to be African pike, catfish and squeakers, up to weights of 2 kg (44 lb). These were caught by the owl watching for ripples in the sheltered inlets, rather than searching the main current of a river. Because of the fish diet and because the roosts are often over water, the pellets are fragile and therefore not so reliable when working out prey items as is the case for most owls.

This classical study pointed out that some descriptions of the vocalisations of Pel's Fishing Owl had been, to put it kindly, fanciful. The sound is not usually produced at dusk; instead the owl waits until about midnight and continues until dawn. The most common call consists of a deep sonorous 'hoommmm-hut' after a gradual build up of grunts, and the call is also concluded with a similar grunting sound. This sequence was described very accurately by Brown, but Liversedge's observations suggest that this is just a contact call used throughout the year, and that as the breeding season approaches owls duet for long periods, integrating their calls so well that it sounds like a continuous burst from a single bird. On nights with a full moon, the owls throats can be seen to vibrate as they call.

Liversedge also described a high-pitched trill, produced to accompany a distraction display in which the female walks out along a branch, as if she were walking the plank, before dropping to the ground and thrashing as if seriously injured.

The breeding season lasts from February to April and egg-laying peaks in March when water levels are at their highest; this ensures that by the time the young are learning to fend for themselves water levels will be low and the fish will be easier to see and catch. The favoured nest site seems to be between 3 and 12 m (10-50 ft) up in ebony trees, which grow well in swamplands. Hollows in the timber are used rather than old nests of other species. Two round white eggs are usually laid in the nest cup which is between 30 and 40 cm (12-15 ½ in) in diameter and lined with debris. The average egg size is 49 × 59 mm (1.9 × 2.3 in). Liversedge is of the opinion that the incubation period, probably carried out by the female alone, is around 33 days. He also noted that only one owlet ever survived and that the second chick either failed to hatch or was eaten soon after emerging.

Initially the chicks are covered with white down, their eyes are closed and they have what Roberts described as tubular nostrils. The owlet's eyes open after about a week; it leaves the nest after about ten weeks but remains with its parents for at least a further four months and possibly much longer. This may confirm Roberts's contention that the young do not attain adult plumage until they are fifteen months old. One question is therefore not yet answered. Does Pel's Fishing Owl begin to breed while still in immature plumage or does it not become sexually mature until its second year?

Liversedge's work deserves to rank alongside that of Peter Steyn, that indefatigable fieldworker who has unravelled so much of the elusive biology of Africa's owls. Reading his accounts of fieldwork, one realises that it is possible to combine scientific fact and beautiful description. Let me conclude the account of this species by sharing Steyn's excitement at the sight of his first Pel's Owl, guided to the spot by Tim Liversedge.

'We had hardly left the camp when he stopped and pointed to a spot high in a leafy tree. I peered up but could see nothing at first, then suddenly a patch of tawny in the shadows had eyes and I was looking at a Pel's Fishing Owl properly for the first time. Through binoculars I could see that its tawny underparts were spotted with black, which provided an effective camouflage in the dappled light, but its large dark eyes set in a rounded head were its most striking feature. I could not see its legs and feet through the leaves but Tim said they were normally hidden by a skirt of loose feathers anyway when the owl was roosting'.

Ussher's or the Rufous Fishing Owl
(*Scotopelia ussheri*)

This elusive species is classified as one of the rarest birds in the world. It is restricted to the rain forests between Ghana and Sierra Leone. It is probably (but not certainly) similar to Pel's Fishing Owl, but it is such an elusive species that it is hard to tell whether it is rare or simply under-recorded. It may well be, however, that it is declining due to the felling of forest and the 'management' of mangrove swamps. Pollution may also be a detrimental factor; the run-off from iron ore mines is affecting the whole of the freshwater ecology in this area. Where there are no fish, there can be no fishing owls.

The Vermiculated Fishing Owl
(*Scotopelia bouvieri*)

This is a similar species to Pel's Fishing Owl, which is found in southern Cameroon, the Congo and northern Angola. Its detailed biology is virtually unknown.

Spectacled Owl   *(Pulsatrix perspicillata)*

CHAPTER NINE

Spectacled, Burrowing, Little, Mottled Owls and Pygmy Owlets

This chapter brings the coverage of owls in the Buboniae sub-family to an end and will consider some 49 species. Some species will be treated rather briefly, but many of these are covered by an extensive literature and interested readers are referred to the Bibliography.

THE GENUS
Pulsatrix

This South American genus is composed of three little-known species.

The Spectacled Owl
(*Pulsatrix perspicillata*)

This owl varies in length from 42.5-47.5 cm (17-19 in). It has no ear tufts and the iris of the eye is yellow. It is dark brown on the upper surface, with a broad white eyebrow. A white area around the bill creates the spectacled effect from which the vernacular name is derived. The throat is white and the face and chest blackish-brown which contrasts sharply with the light buff underparts. The juvenile is one of the strangest-looking owls I have ever seen, with a broad dark brown

mask which, when set against the pale round head, gives it a distinctly monkey-like appearance.

The Spectacled Owl is said to rest by day in the thick foliage of the forest and in second-growth woodland of humid lowlands and foothills, up to a height of 1,230 m (4,000 ft). With this combination of dense cover and difficult terrain, it is not surprising that this owl is rarely seen and may well be more common than has often been thought. Although it is mainly nocturnal, there are diurnal sightings, particularly on dark cloudy mornings and late afternoons.

The call seems to be diagnostic and has been described by Ridgely as being like an imitation of a machine gun; there is also a much slower series of notes consisting of three or four low-pitched hoots which sound like the beating of wings.

Of the breeding biology little is known, apart from the fact that two eggs are laid, usually in a nest hole.

Six sub-species are recognised. *Pulsatrix perspicillata pulsatrix* occurs in eastern Brazil and Paraguay; *Pulsatrix perspicillata boliviana,* as its name implies, is from southern Bolivia and northern Argentina; *Pulsatrix perspicillata perspicillata* occurs throughout the northerly area of South America; *Pulsatrix persicillata chapmani* is found in eastern Costo Rica and western Ecuador, and *Pulsatrix persicillata saturata* is found throughout western Panama and southern Mexico. The sixth sub-species occurs on the island of Trinidad and has been named *Pulsatrix persicillata trinitatis.*

The Tawny-browed Owl
(*Pulsatrix koeniswaldiana*)

This owl is named from the markings over its eyes. So far it has not been divided into races, although it is distributed throughout south Brazil, north Argentina and east Paraguay. There is no reliable data on the species although comparative studies of the Spectacled and Band-bellied Owl suggest a close relationship.

The Band-bellied Owl
(*Pulsatrix melanota*)

This owl is distinguished by dark abdominal banding. It has been separated into two sub-species. *Pulsatrix melanota melanota* occurs throughout eastern Ecuador and Peru, while Bolivia is the home range of *Pulsatrix melanota philoseia*.

THE GENUS
Surnia

The only representative of this genus is the fascinating and well-documented Hawk Owl (*Surnia ulula*). Although it is actually in the size range of 36-41 cm (14-16 in), it can appear much longer due to its habit of perching horizontally rather than upright, which is the more usual posture of owls. The Short-eared Owl (*Asio flammeus*) also perches horizontally but its tail is much shorter than that of the Hawk Owl which often holds its tail at an angle reminiscent of the European Wren *Troglodytes troglodytes*. The flight of the Hawk Owl is very like that of a diurnal hawk and this owl does in fact hunt during daylight. Even the plumage, especially the pale undersurface, heavily barred with grey brown, is hawk-like. The dorsal surface is greyish-brown, heavily mottled with white, and the tail is also obviously barred and appears grey-and-white striped when the bird is perched.

The facial pattern is very distinctive, being pale grey — almost white in some individuals — with a heavy black border, although this does not extend above the eyes. These are small for an owl but their yellow colouring makes them very impressive against the dark feathering of the disc. 'Ear tufts' are lacking and the top of the head, especially when silhouetted against the sky, looks flat. The diurnal hunting, incomplete facial disc and short pointed wings suggest that the Hawk Owl obtains its food by relying upon sight rather than sound. This is confirmed by the fact that the wing feathers lack the structure to insulate against sound, and the air openings in the skull are symmetrically arranged.

The Hawk Owl ranges across central and northern Scandinavia through Finland to northern Russia. It is found all across Asia to the Pacific coast but not beyond the tree line which corresponds to around 65°N. In the USSR the acceptable limit is found where the forest gives way to steppe. In North America the Hawk Owl is found from northern USA and Canada northwards to Alaska. There are no breeding records for Britain but there have been some sightings, during cold winters, as far south as Switzerland. I well remember the fuss caused by a Hawk Owl which turned up near my home at Chipping in Lancashire on 13 September 1959, the day before my birthday. What a present!

With such a wide range it is perhaps surprising to find that only three sub-species have been 'split' from the main stem. *Surnia ulula ulula* is the race found across northern Europe and Asia, *Surnia ulula tianschanica* comes from *Tien Shan*, and the New World race, *Surnia ulula caparoch* comes from northern USA and west and central Canada.

With regard to the feeding pattern of the Hawk Owl, a great deal of information has been gathered, especially from Norway, Sweden and the USSR, through the technique of pellet analysis. These seem to average around 23 × 23 × 60 mm (1 × 1 × 2.4 in) and are mostly recovered from beneath the roost of the male. During the breeding season these have been found within 80 and 160 m (87-175 yd) of the nest site. Mammals, especially voles, form almost 94 per cent of the prey, and it has been proved that, on the whole, the Hawk Owl is a general hunter rather than a specialist, although surveys from the USSR suggest that the bird tends to avoid eating shrews.

This heavy dependence on mammals is only typical of the breeding season. In winter the mammalian proportion of the diet drops below 60 per cent and birds, particularly the willow grouse, become more important. The old idea that the Hawk Owl moved southwards, just like the Snowy Owl (*Nyctea scandiaca*) when the population of Norway Lemmings (*Lemmus lemmus*) declined has been proved to be inaccurate, although a decline in other forms of food supply may cause such a migration. It seems that the southerly limit of the Snowy Owl borders the northern limit of the Hawk Owl and the fact that both species are irruptive during years of low rodent populations may well denote a close relationship.

An examination of diet is more easily carried out than a study of breeding behaviour and, in consequence, there is much less information in this area. It would seem that territories are established some time before breeding commences. Depending upon the range occupied, males can be seen going through their impressive display flights, producing trilling whistle-like notes lasting as long as ten seconds but often seeming to go on longer as they echo through the forest. There is also a soft and surprisingly melodic 'poo-poo, poo-poo' call.

Some workers have also described a wing-clapping display and all agree that the territory held is probably large — but then a large predator will require a substantial area in which to hunt. Hagan in Norway, for example, found only four pairs over an area of some 200 sq.km. (77 sq miles), but whether this reflects choice or scarcity is open to discussion. They do seem to tolerate other birds of prey in close proximity, but are said to be especially aggressive in defence of their nest sites — particularly the male — while the female is incubating or brooding. This aggression is reflected in the birds' choice of perch which is often at the very top of a tree because it is not frightened of being seen.

The choice of nest site is made on the basis of the presence of dense forest (either coniferous or deciduous), preferably close to a marshy area and with a number of clearings, either natural or created by felling, over which to hunt. Old abandoned nests of corvids or birds of prey are sometimes chosen, as are holes in trees, hollow stumps and even nest boxes quite close to farms or forestry buildings. There seems to be disagreement among 'experts' as to whether the nest is lined with feathers or not.

Eggs are usually laid between March and June and the average clutch size is around six. This increases in years when the vole population is high, and it also decreases from north to south. The average size of the white, glossy eggs is 32 × 40 mm (1.3 × 1.6 in). They are incubated by the female alone for a period of around 27 days, beginning with the first egg. This often results in a nest full of owlets of assorted sizes and it is no wonder that both male and female have to take part in the feeding. Mikkola established a fledging period of between 25 and 35 days, the chicks bravely climbing out onto exposed tree branches long before they can fly. They appear to become independent at around three months or so and are able to breed in the year following their birth.

It is said that irruptions of Hawk Owls (the last large movement south being in 1971-72) have become less common during this century. This may be because there are fewer birds these days, and if this is the case, then even more effort is needed to establish their feeding and breeding requirements. These are the only effective tools of the conservationist — ill-informed hearsay is not sufficient.

THE GENUS
Glaucidium

This fascinating genus comprises fifteen species of small owls. The biology of some of these is well documented, while that of others is virtually unknown.

The Eurasian Pygmy Owl
(*Glaucidium passerinum*)

Two sub-species are recognised of this attractive diminutive bird of only 16.5 cm (6½ in). These are *Glaucidium passerinum passerinum,* found in northern Europe and western Asia, and *Glaucidium passerinum orientale,* from eastern Siberia and Manchuria. It is sometimes said that it tends to be under-recorded because of its small size, but there are several other factors involved, including its preference for dense coniferous forest, although in cold weather these owls may approach close to towns and villages. Despite these factors there is enough evidence from workers in the field to attest to the fact that it is indeed thinly distributed.

To a European birdwatcher, however, the Pygmy is a case of once seen never forgotten. It is only the size of a chaffinch, but its yellow eyes glare out from beneath white 'eyebrows', both of which features contrast sharply with the surrounding foliage of conifers such as spruce, larch and pine. The uppersurface is basically mid-brown with pale buff spots, while the undersurface reverses this pattern, being pale grey with darker bandings. The most obvious feature of the species is its huge feet, which account for its ability to kill prey much larger than the casual observer would think possible —lemmings, voles and mice are the main items, with insects also taken during the summer. Some workers, particularly Mikkola (1983) and Bergstedt (1965), have suggested that peak populations of the Pygmy Owl correspond with a peak in numbers of the Bank Vole (*Clethrionomys glareolus*). There also seems to be evidence that this species kills more food than it needs and then hoards the excess in hollow trees or in crevices.

A close examination of a dead specimen will reveal a lack of sound-proofing adaptations on the wing feathers and a facial disc which is less obvious than in many owls. It is therefore known to be a crepuscular hunter, its most active periods being at dawn and dusk.

Living, as it does, deep in dark woodlands, this species needs to be extremely vocal, especially at the onset of the breeding season. At this time high-pitched calls echo through the coniferous areas and to those inexperienced in observing this species, like the author, the 'kuvit' call is very reminiscent of the more familiar Little Owl. This, however, is only one of many calls produced by the pygmy. There is an alarm call of a high and rather weak pitch, sounding like 'tsilp-tsilp', which has been likened by some to the song of the Chiffchaff, (*Phylloscopus collybita*).

There is also one song for spring and another for autumn. The territorial spring song, 'peeu-peeu-peeu', is produced from a perch. During this utterance the bird turns around to create an almost ventriloquilistic quality. The male can also produce a vibrating 'py-py-pyp' sound to which the female is thought to reply in an even higher pitch. Both sexes also have an autumnal song based on the basic 'peeu' unit, but combined in this instance on an ascending scale, and thought by König (1968) to keep the pair in contact over the colder months.

The favoured nest site seems to be in a tree cavity, although if natural holes are at a premium the species has been known to take over nest boxes. The clutch size seems to vary between four and seven, although up to ten and as few as three have been recorded. The eggs are laid at two-day intervals. The average size seems to be 23 × 30 mm (0.9 × 1.2 in). Most workers now accept that incubation is by the female alone and actually begins with the last egg, so that all the owlets hatch together — this is termed synchronous hatching. This does make the calculation of the incubation period rather easier and this is probably in the order of 29 days. The male provides the female with food during this period.

The fledging period is around 27-30 days during this period the male gradually begins to help to feed the young rather than just delivering food to the female. Within about four weeks the young are independent hunters but they may hang around for a much longer period before being 'discouraged' by the parents.

The American Pygmy Owl or Northern Pygmy Owl
(*Glaucidium gnoma*)

This is the North American equivalent of Eurasian Pygmy and their habits and behaviour are broadly similar. It is around 17.5 cm (7½ in) long and is recognised by its rusty or grey-brown plumage and obviously striped breast. When perched, a black patch on either side of the back of the neck is a good field distinction, as is the tail which is held at a jaunty angle — rather wren-like — away from the body. The tail is also longer than in 'normal' owls and the small head is also typical of the Eurasian Pygmy Owl. It is the most widely distributed small 'earless' owl to be found in North America.

The voice is described by Peterson as a rolling series of whistled notes ending with two or three slow deliberate notes, i.e. 'too-too-too-too-too--took--took'. The same worker also suggests that the commonest note is a single 'took' repeated every two or three seconds. This can be quite monotonous, but a census of the species is easily made by listening for this call. The clutch size varies between two and seven. The eggs are laid in a hole in a tree.

At the present time seven sub-species are recognised. *Glaucidium gnoma grinneli* occurs from south-east Alaska to northern California, *Glaucidium gnoma swarthi* is restricted to Vancouver Island, while the race found in central British Columbia and southern California is named *Glaucidium gnoma californicum*. *Glaucidium gnoma pinicola* is found in the central and western areas of the United States and *Glaucidium gnoma cobacense* occurs in Guatemala. This just leaves the nominate race *Glaucidium gnoma gnoma* which is the sub-species found in north and central Mexico.

The Cuban Pygmy Owl
(*Glaucidium siju*)

This a similar but not very well-documented species, of which there are two races. *Glaucidium siju siju* occurs on the island of Cuba and *Glaucidium siju vittatum* is restricted to the Isle of Pines.

The Least Pygmy Owl
(*Glaucidium minutissimum*)

This species is small even by Pygmy Owl standards, being only 13 cm (5 in) long. It has a greyish head covered with small white dots. These spots are absent in young birds. The upper surface is brownish, but there is a broken band of white on the neck, which ends on both sides with a smallish black spot. Occasionally there are a few light spots on the scapulars and wings and this feature has enabled watchers to distinguish individual birds. The pale undersurface is streaked with brown. The tail is black with a number of narrow white bars. The species is active both by day and night, being recognised by a series of up to eight 'poop-poop' calls, and experts are able to call up the bird by imitating this call. The eight sub-species are summarised in Table 16.

The Andean, Mountain or Jardine's Pygmy Owl
(*Glaucidium jardinii*)

These are only two sub-species. *Glaucidium jardinii jardinii* occurs in Colombia, Ecuador, Peru and Venezuela, while the race found in Panama and Costa Rica is *Glaucidium jardinii costaricanum*.

It measures around 15 cm (6 in) and is brown on the uppersurface but with the crown dusted with pale spots, the back spotted and the wings spotted and barred with white and buff. In the immature bird the crown of the head is grey and lacks spots. There is also a short white eyebrow and a small, but surprisingly visible black eye-like spot on both sides of the back of the head. The underside is pale with a band of brown across the chest, occasionally broken in the middle. The tail is dark and marked with narrow white bands. There is also a rufous phase of Jardine's Pygmy Owl. This rufous colour is obvious on the lower surface which also often lacks both bars and streaks.

This owl is found in mountain forests, often above 1,800 m (5,850 ft). It has, probably in error, often been classified as a sub-species of the Ferruginous Pygmy Owl.

The Ferruginous Pygmy Owl
(*Glaucidium brasilianum*)

This has been divided into twelve sub-species (see Table 17). It is very similar to the Common Pygmy Owl (*Glaucidium gnoma*), but the two species are separated by their choice of habitat. Woodlands along river valley bottoms are the favourite habitat for the 16.2 cm (6½ in) long owl.

It is, as its name implies, rufous above, with the crown narrowly streaked with white or buff; the wings are also speckled with white or buff. The breast streakings are brown and the tail, which is black, is narrowly banded with white. The bird has a habit of flicking the tail up and down while perched. Little is known of its biology but the voice has been described as a repetitive 'chu-chu-chu', while Sutton described this as 'chook-chook-chook', repeated up to 40 times with intervals of about a second between each note. This, he said, was reminiscent of a small engine chugging away in the distance.

The Pearl-spotted Owlet
(*Glaucidium perlatum*)

This unmistakable South African owl is distinguished by its tiny size of 18 cm (7 in), by its lack of ear tufts and by the pale spots on its back, from which it takes its vernacular name. The sexes are similar but young birds are almost entirely lacking in spots. The iris is yellow, as are the legs, and the bill is greenish-yellow.

Three sub-species are recognised. *Glaucidium perlatum perlatum* occurs from Senegal to Cameroon, *Glaucidium perlatum kilimense* is from east and north-east Africa, and the South African race is *Glaucidium perlatum licua*.

G. p. licua has been studied in some detail by Peter Steyn, who watched the Pearl-spotted Owl to the north of the Orange River in bushveld habitat, especially in acacia woodland. In his usual lucid style, he described the white spots scattered like raindrops on its head and pointed out that *perlatum* is Latin for 'wearing pearls'.

Prior to the eggs being laid, the female produces a monotonous ventriloquial 'peep' which is answered by the male who brings a regular supply of food as a sort of engagement present. The main items of prey are insects, but the comparatively large feet mean that birds and mammals, which might appear to be too large for the Pearl-spotted Owl to tackle, are also taken. The nest site is usually a natural hole in a tree, or a nest hole made by a woodpecker or a barbet. Roberts noted that the calls were more common in the early evening, which is not surprising as the species is often active during this period. The flight is not silent, a sure sign that this is a diurnal species. The call is a series of notes ascending as 'tu-tu-tu, ti tii' and then descending as 'tia-tia tia tia'.

The white eggs are laid between August and October. The clutch size varies between two and four eggs, their average dimensions being 25 × 31mm (1 × 1.2 in). The incubation period is thought to be 29 days, the female taking charge and the male providing food. Warwick Tarboton noted that the owlets still had their eyes closed ten days after hatching and were covered with greyish-white down. After about a fortnight the eyes open and the quill feathers are already appearing. By 30 days the chicks have been fully feathered for a week and are ready to leave the nest.

The Red-chested Owlet
(*Glaucidium tephronotum*)

This species is closely related to *G. perlatum* but has a rufous breast. Although its natural history has not yet been fully documented, it has been listed as six sub-species, mainly following the examination of musuem specimens. These are *Glaucidium tephronotum tephronotum* from Ghana, *Glaucidium tephronotum pycrafti* from southern Cameroon, *Glaucidium tephronotum medje* from northern Zaire, and *Glaucidium tephronotum lukolelue* from central Zaire, while in eastern Zaire yet another race has been named as *Glaucidium tephronotum kivuense*. Finally, we have a race restricted to Mount Elgon in Kenya — *Glaucidium tephronotum elgonense*.

The Barred Owlet or Owl
(*Glaucidium capense*)

This species has been documented by Peter Steyn, who distinguished it from the Pearl-spotted Owl by its slightly larger size (21 cm/8¼ in), the presence of a much more obvious white wing bar and in that it has bars on its uppersurface, as opposed to spots. Steyn also observed that the tongue and gaps of the Barred Owl were black, while those of the Pearl-spotted Owl were pink. The head is also noticeably larger and rounder when compared to body size, the undersurface is more boldly blotched and there is also a barred gorget which can be seen clearly when the bird is perched. It is defined by Roberts as a fairly common species in the denser areas of bush, especially those near rivers and dominated by acacia.

Its distribution is more restricted than that of the Pearl-spotted Owl but five sub-species have so far been described. *Glaucidium capense capense* is found in southern Africa and Angola, *Glaucidium capense robertsi* occurs in the western regions of Mozambique and Tanzania, and *Glaucidium capense scheffleri* is the race found in south-east Kenya and north-east Tanzania. *Glaucidium capense castaneum* comes from eastern Zaire, while from the south of Zaire and also in north-east Angola we have *Glaucidium costaneum ngamiense*.

The diet consists of small vertebrates and insects, including grasshoppers and caterpillars, which are hunted from a convenient perch, often in daylight — as with many members of this genus, the ability to fly silently is not as advanced as in many of the larger owls. Just after sunset a low bubbling call is produced, probably to keep the pair in contact and there is also a low 'kroo-kroo' call. The alarm call is said to sound like a croaking purr.

The Barred Owl is another hole nester and the average clutch size would seem to be three. The white eggs average 27 × 33 mm (1 × 1.3 in) and are usually laid in September or October. Details of the breeding biology are still lacking but are likely to be similar to those of the Pearl-spotted Owl.

Young Barred Owlets are feathered after about a month, although a few signs of downy feathers still remain, and the head is spotted and not barred — could this be an indicator that there is a close relationship with the Pearl-spotted Owlet? An entry in the South African magazine *Bokmatierie* (27/2/1985) throws further light on the distribution of the species:

'The first Barred Owl *Glaucidium capense* known to science was collected in 1824 in the Eastern Cape by Sir Andrew Smith, who, in the same area, 'shot in depths of one of the forests' a second specimen several years later. For about one and a half centuries subsequently, records of this species from the Eastern Cape were mysteriously absent.

The Barred Owl is generally considered a tropical species, distributed from Angola and northern Botswana eastwards to Tanzania and southwards to the eastern portion of southern Africa. In some areas, such as the Okavango Delta, it is common, easily detected by its call, and may even be observed hunting during daylight. It does not necessarily hide itself by day as do Scops Owls (*Otus senegalensis*) and Wood Owls (*Strix woodfordii*).

The fact that the species had not been collected or recorded south of Durban since the time of Smith led to the belief by some in the 1960s that the original type specimen had, in fact, been obtained from a locality other than the Eastern Cape, or that the birds were extinct in that area. Dr P. Clancey, however, in 1968, stated that there was "no reason to doubt the continued existence of a discrete . . . form of Barred Owlet in this region." The accuracy of this prediction was bought home to the ornithological world with a jolt when, in March 1980, a dead adult Barred Owl was found next to a house in Kenton-on-Sea and was identified by Graeme Arnott, who sent the valuable specimen to the Durban Musuem. The specimen provided further evidence of the presence of a living population in the area; the owl matched the painting by Smith of 1839 far

more closely than did the specimens from the tropics. Furthermore, it was found very near to the locality in the Bathurst district from which the type specimen is thought to have been obtained. Only one and a half years later, on 17 August 1981 a Barred Owl was photographed during daytime at the Hluleka Nature Reserve on the Transkei coast by D. W. Kurtz.'

The Barred Jungle Owlet
(*Glaucidium radiatum*)

This is divided into two sub-species, *Glaucidium radiatum radiatum* from Southern India and Sri Lanka, and *Glaucidium radiatum melabaricum* from south-west India.

About 20 cm (8 in) long, this species has a round head and body without ear tufts, a combination which produces a dumpy little owl. The uppersurface is dark brown, but obviously barred in pale rufous, while the undersurface is pale with the abdomen and mid-breast regions white — the rest of the undersurface is in dark olive. There is also a white chin and moustache-like stripe. In flight there is an obvious reddish patch on the underwing.

Its preferred habitat is mixed moist deciduous forest and areas in the foothills dominated by bamboo and teak. They are seldom seen above the 2,000-m (650-ft) contour. This jungle owlet tends to occur singly or in pairs and is crepuscular, being active an hour or so prior to dusk and dawn, although on wet dull days it may be active during daylight. On bright days it roosts among foliage or even deep in a hollow tree to avoid being mobbed by small birds which, along with small mammals, lizards and insects, make up its diet.

The call begins with a loud 'kao' repeated slowly several times, followed by a faster 'kao-kut, kao-kuk kao-kuk' lasting about five seconds and fading towards the end. During the call the owlet hunches its shoulders, nods its head and wags its tail, movements which also seem to impart a ventriloquistic quality to the voice. A breeding call 'cur-cur-cur' has also been described.

The breeding season lasts from March to May. An old nest left by a woodpecker or a barbet may be chosen, but the more usual site is a natural tree hole between 3 and 8 m (10-26 ft) from the ground. Apart from the clutch size, which is three or four white eggs measuring 27×31.5 mm (1.1 ×1 ¼in), very little is known of the breeding biology.

The Collared Pygmy Owl or Owlet
(*Glaucidium brodiei*)

This owl is 17 cm (6½ in) long and is described by Salim Ali and Ripley as a 'charming diminutive owl' which is very diurnal in habit and usually to be seen perched on its own, on a thinly foliaged branch close to the trunk of a tall forest tree. Not only does it hunt in daylight, it also calls during this time. Because of this daytime activity, it is probably mobbed more often than other species. It is thought that markings on the back of the head, which look remarkably like eyes and a bill, may discourage attack from the rear. This peculiar system of markings is also a feature of the Pearl-spotted Owlet from South Africa (see page 71).

There is every reason why small birds should combine their efforts to chase away the Collared Pygmy Owlet because, for its size, it is a deadly predator, chasing its prey in a series of rapid wing beats interspersed with gliding pauses. It carries small birds in its huge-taloned feet to a perch where they are held down with one foot and torn to pieces with the bill in the manner used by a falcon.

The species is recognised by its grey-brown barred plumage, an obvious pale eye-stripe and a reddish half-collar on the upper back, from which it takes its vernacular name. It is this feature which forms part of the owl-like face on the back of the species. The white throat patch is also an obvious and diagnostic feature, and there is a rufous phase which seems to be a feature of all four of the sub-species. *Glaucidium brodiei brodiei* occurs from the Himalayas to northern Indochina and Malaysia, *Glaucidium brodiei pardalotum* occurs in Taiwan, *Glaucidium brodiei pentum* is found in Sumatra, and *Glaucidium brodiei borneense* is the race confined to Borneo. It frequents areas of open hill forests of rhododendron, oak, fir or deodar and seems happy up to altitudes of 3,200 m (10,000 ft).

The breeding season extends from March to June but peaks during April and May. The favoured nest site is an unlined natural hollow between 2 and 10 m (6½-33ft) high. This nest can be surprisingly large, but there are also records of the owl taking over the nest of a barbet or a woodpecker.

The call used to keep the pair in contact is described as a four-syllable bell-like whistling 'toot...toot-toot...toot...' joined in sequences of three or four bursts which are repeated at regular intervals. While calling the bird bobs up and down and is thus able to produce a ventriloquial effect.

The clutch size varies from three to five, the white eggs averaging 24 × 29 mm (0.9 × 1.1 in). Very little is known about the breeding biology, such as incubation time, fledging period or the part played by the sexes.

Cuckoo Owl
(*Glaucidium cuculoides*)

This is divided into ten sub-species (see Table 18), but a thorough study of their classification and breeding biology is yet to be made. At 23 cm (9 in), the Cuckoo Owl is larger than the Barred Jungle Owl. Hornless and dumpy, it is olive to dark brown above and clearly barred with white. The abdomen is white but bears dark longitudinal striations. There is also a white throat patch which can be seen as the owl perches on dead trees in broad daylight, waiting to pounce on passing prey. This consists of small mammals and birds, plus a significant proportion of insects, especially beetles and grasshoppers.

The call can be heard at any time throughout the day, but is at its most vocal at dawn and for the first couple of hours after the sun rises. Osmaston described the sound as harsh squeaks sounding 'as if the bird was trying to rise to some great effort which ends suddenly'. In the breeding season Salim Ali has described a continuous bubbling, but quite musical whistle 'wowowowowo', lasting between four and seven seconds and often repeated.

The breeding season is from late March to May. The nest is placed in an abandoned woodpecker's hole or, preferably, a natural cavity. The clutch size is normally four white eggs, the average size is being 36 × 31 mm (1.2 × 1.4 in). It is thought, but not proved, that both sexes incubate, but little else is known.

Sjostedt's Barred Owlet
(*Glaucidium sjostedti*)

This owlet occurs in the forest areas of West and Central Africa where it feeds on insects and small vertebrates. It possibly lays only one egg, in a tree hole. Apart from its size, of around 20 cm (8 in) we know little about it. There are no sub-species.

The Albertine Owlet
(*Glaucidium albertinum*)

This is one of the world's rarest birds and has been classified on the basis of five specimens, one from Rwanda and four from the forests of east Zaire.

THE GENUS
Xenoglaux

This genus is represented only by the Long-whiskered Owlet (*Xenoglaux loweryi*) from north Peru, and has been described from only three specimens.

THE GENUS
Micrathene

This genus is also represented by only one species, the Elf Owl (*Micrathene whitneyi*) of which we have a rather more detailed description, although there are still surprising gaps in our knowledge. Four sub-species are recognised. *Micrathene whitneyi whitneyi* is found in the south-west states of the USA and north-west Mexico, *Micrathene whitneyi idonea* is found in Texas and central Mexico. *Micrathene whitneyi sandfordi* comes from Baja California, and *Micrathene whitneyi graysoni* is found on Socorro Island.

At 15 cm (6 in), this sparrow-sized owl can be recognised by its reddish-brown underparts and white eyebrows. It is found mainly in deserts where the Sahuaro Cactus grows, but it has also been recorded at heights of up to 1,700 m (5,520 ft). It hides away during the day in holes in the cactus, probably to escape the heat as much as the light, and emerges at night, when it is quite vocal. It produces a high-pitched 'whi-whi-whi-whi-whi' which, should it become disturbed, is interspersed with rapidly descending notes 'teeok-teeok-teeok'. Its main food would seem to be insects

and the nest is sited in a hole in a cactus or a tree. The clutch size varies from four to six and apparently both sexes incubate for about a fortnight.

THE GENUS
Uroglaux

This contains only one very rare species, the Papuan Hawk Owl (*Uroglaux dimorpha*) which is found in New Guinea and Japan. It is thought to prefer a forest habitat and to feed on insects and rodents, but beyond these scanty facts little else is known.

THE GENUS
Ninox

Here we have a collection of eighteen species which are well represented in Australia. Although information on some species is scanty, there is enough data to allow some understanding of the genus.

The Rufous Owl
(*Ninox rufa*)

This owl is some 50 cm (20 in) long and a most powerful bird, feeding on mammals and also upon insects. There are, at the present time, four recognised sub-species. *Ninox rufa rufa* is found throughout northern Australia, and *Ninox rufa queenslandica* in eastern Queensland. These two sub-species have been studied rather more than the Aru Island race, *Ninox rufa aruensis*, or *Ninox rufa humeralis*, which is found on Waigeu Island and New Guinea.

As its vernacular name implies, this mainly nocturnal species has a distinctly rufous appearance, especially on the breast which is heavily banded with rufous colouring.

This owl tends to stay hidden during the day, in areas of dense foliage, preferably skirting a river valley. At night it hunts on silent wings among clearings in the forest. The call note has been described as 'hoo-hoooo', repeated at regular intervals. The nest is usually situated in a hollow tree and the clutch size is normally between two and three. The breeding season lasts from July to September.

The Powerful Owl
(*Ninox strenua*)

This owl is monotypic (there are no sub-species) and is indeed well named. It is around 60 cm (24 in) long and inhabits eastern Queensland, New South Wales and eastern and southern Victoria. During the day these owls roost close to trees or deep in vegetation, but at night they emerge to feed upon birds and mammals. The nest is sited in a tree hole, and the clutch of two or three white, rounded eggs is incubated by the female for about one month, during which time the male keeps her well supplied with food. The breeding season seems to peak in November. Once the young have hatched (they are blind at first), they are provided with food by both parents. Initially the prey is dismembered and pieces touched against their bills to make the chicks aware of the fact that food has arrived. An interesting piece of behaviour occurs when there is a surplus of food — it is wrapped up neatly in its skin again and offered later when the chicks are hungry once more.

The Barking or Winking Owl
(*Ninox connivens*)

This species is divided into seven sub-species (see Table 19) and its precise classification has given taxonomists problems for many years; complete agreement has yet to be reached. Its horrendous call, is however, well known to many fieldworkers, although this cry was once attributed to the Powerful Owl. It has been likened to the call of a woman being murdered, and local names for the species have included 'the screaming woman owl' and 'murder bird'.

Barking Owls which are 45 cm (18 in) long, occur singly or in pairs. They prefer open woodland or areas of scrub. In the daytime they remain hidden in thick foliage or even in hollow trees; should they be seen in full daylight they are mobbed by small birds, and during this disturbance they produce a loud grunting noise. Their normal call — they seem to use the 'murder call' sparingly, for which those camping in woodlands are doubtless grateful — is described as 'kerr-kerr-kerr-koo-wook'. This is heard when the owl is hunting for mammals and small birds, although a substantial part of the diet consists of insects. A sign that the mating season is imminent can be detected when a 'hoo-woo-woo' or 'kioew' call is produced.

Hollow trees are the preferred nesting site, although there are a significant number of records of nests in rabbit burrows. The average clutch size is two or three round white eggs, which is a normal clutch number for owls. What is not usual is that the eggs are reported to be laid on a bed of down feathers. The breeding season lasts from August to September, the incubation period of about one month being undertaken by the hen alone. The male provides food for her, however, and once the eggs have hatched both sexes play an equal part in rearing the young. When the owlets first hatch they are covered with soft white down and their eyes are closed.

The Boobook Owl or Morepoke Owl
(*Ninox novaeseelandiae*)

This is divided into fifteen sub-species (see Table 20). This species has been taxonomically confusing for many years, but some semblance of order is now appearing.

Its length is around 40 cm (15½ in), although the hen is larger than the cock. Pairs are found in woodlands throughout Australia. The upperparts are dark brown with white mottling on the wings. The undersurface is cinnamon and buff streaked with white. The chin is white and the legs are feathered. The bill is slate coloured and the eyes are yellowish. These birds are also recognised by their very long wings. They can be a little difficult to census because they hide away in hollow trees, rock crevices or among dense foliage. Towards dusk they come out and call their name — 'boobook' or, as some people prefer to hear it, 'mopoke! mopoke!.' Their food is mainly small birds, mammals and especially insects.

The nest is sited in a hollow tree and it is reported that a bed of twigs and feathers is provided for the three or four white round eggs. The parents are resident, but following breeding the young disperse over a wide area.

The breeding season lasts from September until January. Incubation is by the female only, but she is fed throughout the 33-day period by the male. The two feed the young together for 40 days it takes them to fledge.

At one time the Spotted Boobook Owl was classified as a separate species, but it is now thought to be the most easily identified of all the sub-species, *Ninox novaeseelandiae ocellata*. It is a much smaller bird than the nominate race, being only 35 cm (14 in) long. As its name suggests, it is spotted on the back, crown and nape, with the breast also distinctly marked.

The Brown Hawk Owl
(*Ninox scutulata*)

As its name implies this owl is very hawk-like in appearance. There are ten recognised sub-species (see Table 21).

It is dark grey above, but the forehead is white and there are irregular white patches on the shoulders. The throat and foreneck are fulvous and streaked with brown, while the rest of the underparts are white but marked by large red-brown spots which form broken bars. The tail is barred with black and tipped with white. The preferred habitat is well-wooded country or that with a few groves of trees, especially if a watercourse is running through it. These owls seem quite happy to put up with the presence of human settlement providing the correct habitat is available.

This owl is defined as crepuscular or nocturnal, but will move around in daylight if disturbed, its wing beat being fast and hawk-like. It tends to have a favoured perch, such as a post or tree stump, from which it hunts by darting out, taking an insect in flight and returning to the perch, in the manner of a European flycatcher. Its flight has also been likened to that of a nightjar. The Hawk Owl is also thought to catch the occasional bat or bird by this method.

The sound it produces is distinctive, being described as a soft musical 'oo...uk...oo...uk...oo...ouk', usually uttered in runs of between ten and sixteen phrases, at the rate of about one every second and with a short gap between. On moonlit nights this can go on for long periods, both birds joining in what amounts to a love duet. In overcast weather the performance may be carried on well into the day.

The breeding season stretches from March to June. The nest site is usually a hollow tree. Three, four or, on the odd occasion, five round white eggs are produced, with average measurements of 30 × 35 mm (1.2 × 1.4 in). These are believed to be incubated mainly by the female, although with some assistance from the male. The incubation period is not firmly established, but 24 days has been suggested. The fledging period is not accurately known. Both male and female share in the feeding of the owlets.

The Andaman Brown Hawk Owl
(*Ninox affinis*)

This owl is apparently restricted to the Andaman and Nicobar Islands in the Philippines and, although three sub-species have been recognised from museum skins, little accurate breeding data are available. The three sub-species are *Ninox affinis affinis* from the Andaman Islands, *Ninox affinis isolata* from Nicobar Island, and *Ninox affinis rexpimenti* from Great Nicobar Island.

The length is about 28 cm (11 in) and the plumage is obviously brown, with very bright rufous spotting on the undersurface. The iris is yellow, as are the feet which end in black claws, while the bill is mainly black but with greenish tinges on the culmen and tips of the bill. One record of this bird's feeding technique was noted by Davison, who actually shot one while it was hawking moths like a nightjar in low secondary jungle during the late evening.

The remaining twelve species making up the *Ninox* genus are so little known that they have simply been listed in Table 22, along with their sub-species.

THE GENUS
Gymnoglaux

Only one species, the Bare-legged Owl (*Gymnoglaux lawrencii*) has been placed in this genus. It is divided into two races, *Gumnoglaux lawrencii lawrencii* from central and eastern Cuba, and *Gymnoglaux lawrencii excus* from the west of Cuba and the Isle of Pines. Nothing is known of the biology of the species.

THE GENUS
Sceloglaux

Here again we find a genus represented by only one species and even this may be extinct. This is (or was) the White-faced or Laughing Owl (*Sceloglaux albifacies*) from New Zealand's South Island. Apparently it inhabited open country and nested under boulders. Two eggs were laid and incubated by the female only for 25 days.

THE GENUS
Athene

Three, or perhaps four, species make up this genus of Little Owls, and we do know a great deal about them, especially the first to be described.

The Little Owl
(*Athene noctua*)

This is divided into fifteen sub-species, which are summarised in Table 23. The race found in central Europe is *Athene noctua vidalii* and the description which follows is based upon this. When this sub-species was scientifically named in 1857, Ignatius Vidal was the director of the Zoological Museum of Valencia, and it was he who first described it from a museum specimen. (See page 23.)

Around 22 cm (8½ in) long, this is the smallest owl to be found in Great Britain although it is not considered to be native as it was deliberately introduced from the Netherlands in an effort to reduce agricultural pests, hence its alternative name of the Dutch Owl.

A first abortive attempt was made to introduce the Little Owl to Yorkshire in 1824, and more successful introductions were made into Kent (40 birds) in 1874, which led to breeding in 1879 and, with 'top-ups' on a regular basis, the Little Owl was firmly established by 1896. The real focal point of the introductions, however, was Northamptonshire, where large numbers were released between 1888 and 1890, and from where they have spread into most areas of England and Wales and are now colonising southern Scotland. Only the occasional vagrant has reached Ireland.

These introductions were not made without controversy, as breeders of pheasants and chickens and the owners of grouse moors were very much against the introduction of the Little Owl which they looked upon as an unwanted predator. As a study of the diet indicates, these objections were, on the whole, unfounded.

The present British population is between 7,000 and 15,000 breeding pairs. Some workers have suggested that the Little Owl was once native to Britain but then became extinct. A fossil found at Chudleigh in Devon, however, dated to the Pleistocene period (see Table 1), has been shown by Harrison to be a bone from a Sparrowhawk (*Accipiter nisus*) and not, as was often suggested, that of a Little Owl. The Little Owls do, however, seem to have been present in Britain some 500,000 years ago during an interglacial period.

The Little Owl is often described as being liver-coloured with the upperparts mottled with white. On the round head there are pale streaks and the wings and tail are barred with brown and white. The facial disc is present, but is not well developed and the upper area has pale feathers which give the impression of prominent horizontal eyebrows, from beneath which the pale yellow eyes beam out like headlights. The round shape of the head is accentuated by the lack of ear tufts. The legs are comparatively long, and I saw these in action one wet evening when a Little Owl ran across the road in front of my car at a staggering speed. The feet are perfectly adapted for catching insects and the legs are covered with down which may well give protection when the Little Owl tackles small mammals which can give a sharp bite. In flight, the Little Owl's round broad wings and short tail are obvious features.

Little Owls begin their breeding season early in the year, often in February, the onset being greeted by a 'kiew-kiew-kiew' call. This is produced while perched on a wall or in a tree and has been likened by some to the sound of a Curlew (*Numenius arquata*). The male can also produce a gentle 'hoo-oo hooo-oo' call, which is often answered by the female's high-pitched shrieking. The female may be pursued by the male or she may stand still and be fed by her mate prior to copulation.

A suitable cavity is selected as the nest site and this can be in a stone wall or hollow tree forming part of a hedge in a park or garden. Disused nests of corvids are also sometimes used. In Britain most eggs are laid between April and May, with up to seven being laid, although the average clutch is around four. The incubation period is now thought to be around 30 days, the female doing the work but being fed by the male. The difficulty involved in field observations is highlighted by the fact that even in such a well-documented species, it is still not certainly established whether the male does actually sit on the eggs occasionally. Further, some workers also feel that the incubation period may be as short as 24 days. I think that confusion may have arisen because some females seem to begin their incubation with the laying of the first egg, while others wait until the clutch is complete. Both parents do, however, take an active role in feeding the owlets until they fledge, some 35 days after hatching.

Less work has been carried out on the analysis of Little Owl pellets than on those of many of the larger European owls, probably because they are smaller and are also spread more generally around the territory, plus the fact that they contain large amounts of insect material which is difficult to identify. Insects are the main items in the diet, especially beetles, but birds such as the Starling (*Sturnus vulgaris*), House Sparrow (*Passer domesticus*), and commonly occurring members of the thrush family are frequently taken during the breeding season. It must also be admitted that the occasional — and I would stress the word 'occasional' — game chick is also taken, as well as a number of small mammals. During the summer 40 per cent of the British Little Owl's food requirements are met by small mammals, but in Italy as much as 98 per cent of the diet consists of insects. This is obviously an indication that the Little Owl is an opportunist feeder, which is the secret of the success of many owls.

The Spotted Little Owl
(*Athene brama*)

This is a similar species, divided into four sub-species *Athene brama brama*, the nominate race, is found in southern India, *Athene brama albida* is from Iran, *Athene brama indica* is found in the northern and central regions of India, while the race from Burma to south-west Indochina is *Athene brama pulchra*.

The nominate sub-species is described by Salim Ali as a squat greyish owl, spotted with white and with a comparatively large round head, without 'ear tufts' and with yellow eyes. Is is 21 cm (8 in) long and is found around villages, ruined houses and mango trees but it tends to avoid heavy forest. It is found in pairs or family groups of three or four. It is seen hunting at dawn, dusk and in full daylight, which can lead on occasions to it being mobbed by small birds.

The hunting technique is to select a perch from which the Spotted Little Owl launches forth to seize insects — termites being a favourite prey. They have been seen hovering — albeit rather clumsily — over suitable prey. They often use street lamps as perches and then launch forth to grab insects, especially moths, which are attracted as soon as the light is lit in the evening.

The voice is a harsh screeching 'chirrurr-chirrurr-chirruir', which may be alternated with a discordant-sounding 'cheevak-cheevak-cheevak'. As the breeding season approaches, the species becomes increasingly more vocal.

The breeding season stretches from February to April. A natural hole in a tree trunk or a hole in a wall is a favourite nesting site, although holes in the roofs of houses are also accepted at times. The clutch size varies from three to six, the white eggs averaging 27 × 32 mm (1.1 × 1.3 in). It is thought that the nest may be lined by both sexes with leaves and feathers, but this has not been proved. Neither have the incubation and fledging periods been established, although most observers think the sexes share the duties.

The Forest Spotted Owlet
(*Athene blewitti*)

This owl is 23 cm (9 in) long. It resembles the Spotted Owlet but is larger and its wings are much shorter by comparison. The whole of the uppersurface is an earthy brown, but with an ill-defined hind collar of white spots. Across the throat is a dark brown band. The undersurface is light brown and there are white fringes on many of the feathers. It is monotypic (the only member of the species) and considered to be rare in central India. Salim Ali noted that between its discovery in 1873 and 1976 less than a dozen specimens had been collected. This probably does reflect rarity, but it must be remembered that this owl lives in damp areas heavily covered with deciduous jungle and wild mango swamps — difficult terrain in which to carry out reliable census work. Not surprisingly, little is known of its breeding biology.

The Burrowing Owl
(*Athene cunicularia*)

This owl may be wrongly classified here, as recent workers have tended to create a new genus for it, and name it *Speotyto cunicularia*, the only member of the genus. The present author may perhaps be excused for hedging his bets. The nineteen sub-species are listed in Table 24.

The species is recognised as a small brown bird with long legs, standing, mammal-like on a mound of earth and fixing anything that moves with a steely glare from its huge yellow eyes. It was formerly abundant on the grasslands of the United States, but also extends into the seaside sand dune areas and the first few miles of deserts. At around 23 cm (9 in), it resembles the European Little Owl, but the legs look even longer in this agile species. The legs and feet are perfectly adapted not only for killing but also for burrowing. These owls will kill and also take over the burrows of rodents, prairie dogs and ground squirrels. A substantial number of insects are also eaten.

They may even breed and roost in drainage pipes close to human residential districts. There does not seem to be any evidence to support the suggestion made by the makers of the so-called spaghetti Western films that this owl shares a hole with a rattlesnake. It is thought, however, that a frightened owl is able to produce a sound very like that of the dreaded 'rattler', which would certainly deter potential predators.

The normal call, however, is a mellow but high-pitched 'coo-coo-coo'. These notes bring the birds into breeding condition, and they seem quite capable of digging their own nest burrow which can be up to 3 m (10 ft) long and ends in a circular cavity which is lined with grass or manure. Manure is also reported to be placed near the entrance, probably in an effort to confuse mammalian predators.

The clutch size varies from three to ten, but is usually above five. The eggs are laid between April and August, peaking in May. They are white and glossy, but soon stain while they are being incubated by the female for about 22 days. During this time she is fed by the male. The male will return to the same breeding hole for several years, but may breed with different females — he should thus know the surrounding hunting area well enough to provide sufficient food for his growing family. The owlets can fly in about a month and are independent around nine weeks. Like most owls they are capable of breeding in the year following their birth.

THE GENUS
Ciccaba

In this final genus of the Buboninae family there are five species.

The Mottled Owl
(*Ciccaba virgata*)

This is a medium-size species about 35 cm (14 in) without ear tufts. It has brown eyes and is brown above, mottled with grey and dusky brown, with a prominent white eye stripe. The undersurface is paler but mottled and streaked with dark brown. The tail and wings are dusky but mottled and barred with pale grey. There is a recognisable dark phase but the variation within the species is such that eight sub-species have been described (see Table 25). It is fairly common in forest and second growth woodland, ranging into woodlands to around 2,000 m (6,500 ft). It is, however, very nocturnal which makes it difficult to census. Eisenmann has described its voice as a long-drawn-out, almost cat-like screech 'keeoweeyo' or 'cowoaooo' and there is a 'grrr' growling noise. There is also a low deep 'whoo-oo' modulated downwards and usually repeated three times.

Two similar species are found in the same areas, but the Mottled Owl can be distinguished from the Black-and-white Owl which, as its name implies, is distinctly barred on the undersurface in black and white. The other similar species, the Striped Owl (*Rhinoptynx clamator*), (see page 91) has prominent ear tufts and is found in open country rather than in the depths of forests.

The Black-and White Owl
(*Ciccaba nigrolineata*)

This owl is around 37.5 cm (15 in) long. It has sooty black upperparts, against which a broken white eye stripe stands out clearly. The throat is also black and the remaining undersurface is white, narrowly banded with black. This owl is described as uncommon. It is local in forests and bordering scrublands, often up to 2,000 m (6,500 ft), occurring from southern Mexico to western Ecuador.

Little is yet known of its breeding biology, although the voice of this mainly nocturnal bird has been studied. Two distinct calls have been identified. One is a long-drawn-out nasal 'oo-weh' with an upward inflection. The other is described as a very deep resonant 'whoof-whoof-whoof'. There are no sub-species.

The Black-banded owl
(*Ciccaba huhula*)

This owl is also monotypic. It is found from the Guianas to central and southern Brazil. Few details are available regarding its natural history as is also the case with the next species.

The Rufous-banded Owl
(*Ciccaba albitarsus*)

This is represented by two sub-species, namely *Ciccaba albitarsus albitarsus*, found in Colombia, Ecuador and Venezuala, and *Ciccaba albitarsus tertia*, found in Bolivia.

The African Wood Owl
(*Ciccaba woodfordii*)

This owl varies in length from 30 to 36 cm (12-14 in), females being larger than their mates. It lacks ear tufts and the background colour varies from very dark brown to deep russet. The sexes are similar in colour but the young are much paler. It is fairly common in some areas but localised in others, preferring dense forests and bush where it can be seen sitting close to the main trunks of trees and in the deep foliage of bushes. There are also records of sightings in the suburbs of Cape Town.

The voice is distinctive. The Zulus describe one phrase as 'weh mamah' which means 'oh my mother'. The call has also been 'translated' as 'who are you?'.

The breeding biology was not unravelled until fairly recently, when the work of Jo Scott established the following details. The season is from August to October. The clutch size varies from one to three white eggs, there being a gap of about 36 hours between each laying. The average size of the egg is 37 × 44 mm (1.4 × 1.7 in). Incubation is by the female only but she is fed throughout the 31-day period by the male, who brings mice, small birds, frogs and large numbers of insects.

The owlets quit the nest between 30 and 37 days following hatching, but at this stage they do not fly very well. They remain dependent upon their parents for around four months after leaving the nest and may have to be 'encouraged' to leave the parents' territory prior to the start of the next breeding cycle. A pair may well use the same site, which may be a tree hole or a depression on the ground, for many years.

Tawny Owl   (*strix aluco*)   *photograph by John Hawkins*

CHAPTER TEN

The Strix Owls

This and the next chapter will consider the second sub-family of owls — the Striginae. There are twelve species of *Strix* owls — the Wood or Tawny Owls — some of which have been more thoroughly documented than any other group of owls.

Hume's Owl
(*Strix butleri*)

In books published before 1980 there were only three specimens of the species available for description. How things have changed! This is a desert owl and therefore unlikely to be seen very often. It seems that in suitable habitats the species can be almost common. In the desert lands of Palestine they inhabit the wadis leading down towards the valley of the Dead Sea and they also occur, according to Jennings, in Saudi Arabia and Oman. In 1981 47 sites were recorded in Israel by Leshem, and Aronson, in 1979, noted that fifteen Hume's Owls had been killed on the roads between 1973 and 1978. This may be due to this owl's habit of waiting by the side of roads for mammalian prey to cross.

Hume's Owl and the Tawny Owl are similar species but are dissimilar in habitat — trees for one and desert for the other. It would seem, therefore, that the owl referred to in Isaiah 34 : 14 is likely to be Hume's.

'The wild beasts of the desert shall also meet with the wild beasts of the island and the satyr shall cry to his fellow: the Screech Owl also shall rest there and find for herself a place to rest.'

Hume's Owl is dark brown-buff covered with darker streaks. On the lower nape there is a golden-brown area which resembles a collar. The tail and flight feathers are barred with buff and black-brown. The facial disc is grey and the underparts are pale but tinged with orange, particularly on the breast. Early museum specimens were described as having dark eyes, but yellow-orange eyes have been described in recent times. The body size is around 30 cm (12 in) but there is some variation, perhaps due to the fact that females are slightly larger than the males.

Although few details are available regarding the breeding biology, it is thought that they use holes in rocks, buildings or in the odd isolated patch of trees such as juniper. Egg-laying is thought to begin in January and lasts until April. Calling certainly reaches a peak at this time. Starting some twenty minutes after sunset, it can go on monotonously all night. 'Hoooo-huhu-huhu' and 'whoo-who-whoo' are softly called and are similar to the sound of a Tawny Owl. At a distance the call can be confused with that of a dove.

Because of the collection and study of pellets, we perhaps know more about its food than we do about other aspects of its biology. Rock Gerbils (*Gerbillus dasyurus*) are an important item — mammals forming almost 50 per cent of the diet — while small birds, reptiles and insects are also taken.

The Spotted Wood Owl
(*Strix seloputo*)

This is a forest owl from south-east Asia. It is an under-recorded species which feeds mainly on beetles. Three sub-species have been described. One, *Strix seloputo seloputo*, occurs from southern Burma to southern Indochina and in Malaysia and Java. The other two have a more restricted range; *Strix seloputo baweana* is confined to the island of Bawean, and *Strix seloputo wiepkeni* is the race from the island of Palawan. It is thought to live in deep forest, feed mainly on insects, especially beetles, and lay either one or two round white eggs.

The Mottled Wood Owl
(*Strix ocellata*)

This Indian species is now divided into three sub-species, namely *Strix ocellata ocellata* from the Himalayas and northern India, *Strix ocellata grandis* from western India, and *Strix ocellata grisescens* from north and central India. In length it is around 48 cm (19 in).

The ear tufts are missing, which gives the head a soft, rounded appearance. It is vermiculated and mottled above with an attractive and variable mixture of black, white, buff, brown and rufous. The facial disc is well developed and pale, but with concentric barring in black. The throat is chestnut and black but stippled liberally with white. There is a white half-collar on the neck, which makes the species easily recognised. The rest of the undersurface is buff-coloured (almost white in some individuals) but narrowly barred with black. In flight the large area of yellowish-buff on the wings is clearly seen and I once heard this species described as a Tawny Owl gone rusty! The eyes are dark brown.

This species is largely nocturnal, the paired birds spending the day in deep cover huddled together against a tree trunk. They are, however, perfectly able to fly around in daylight and can even catch food at this time if conditions so dictate. Rodents, birds, lizards, amphibians and large insects are all taken, and Ali reports the presence of a scorpion, complete with its sting, in the stomach of a dead owl. Was it shot or stung to death one wonders?

The call is produced just before emergence from the daytime roost and has been described as an eerie sound. It is a loud and quavering 'choohuoo-a' which is more common at dusk and again at dawn, although it is produced occasionally throughout the night. It is also at its loudest and most insistent during the breeding season, which is between November and April. Outside the breeding season a single mellow, metallic hoot is produced and it has also been said to produce a loud scream, rather reminiscent of that of the Barn Owl. Bill-snapping has also been recorded.

The nest is usually in a hollow tree, but there is a record of the birds building a stick nest. We have to ask, however, if this is a reliable observation, or had the pair simply taken over the nest of a corvid. There seems to be no record of lining the nest prior to the production of the clutch of two or three eggs. These are round, creamy white and the average size is 43 × 51 mm (1.7 × 2 in). The details of the breeding cycle are, however, not well documented.

The Brown Wood Owl
(*Strix leptogrammica*)

This species is widely distributed throughout India, east Java and Borneo and has been divided into fifteen sub-species (see Table 26). In length it is around 53 cm (21 in). It is a truly brown owl, with obviously barred underparts and a pale facial disc surmounted and highlighted by brown. There are no ear tufts but there is an obvious white eye stripe. The scapulars, wings and upper tail coverts are barred with white. The chin area is a subtle mixture of chocolate and white, while the most obvious ventral feature is a white throat patch. The remainder of the lower plumage is a pale fulvous or buff-white closely covered with dark brown bars.

The Brown Wood Owl is said to be very shy and spends the daytime in dense woodlands. It has occasionally been recorded at heights of up to 4,000 m (13,000 ft). A pair often roosts together. It is nocturnal and has a very silent flight. It feeds upon rodents, birds, reptiles and amphibians. Some workers have suggested, but without clear proof, that it also takes fish.

The voice is described as a mellow musical 'tok-too-hoo', repeated every few seconds, especially during moonlit nights. Bill-snapping is also recorded frequently, as are a variety of shrieks and chuckles.

The breeding season lasts from January to March, the chosen site being the fork of a tree, hollow or a scrape at the foot of a tree or cliff. The normal clutch size is two, or perhaps only one, round white egg measuring 46 × 56 mm (1.8 × 2.2 in). Details of the breeding cycle are not fully understood, but are likely to be similar to those of the Tawny Owl.

The Tawny Owl or Brown Owl
(*Strix aluco*)

This is one of the most studied of all owls. It is divided into thirteen sub-species which are summarised in Table 27. The British and Western European sub-species is *Strix aluco sylvatica* and it is to this that the following description applies, although the other sub-species will only show slight variations. The word *strix* derives from the Greek *strizo*, meaning 'to screech', and this certainly applies to one of the world's most vocal owls.

There is a variety of calls, including a soft trembling and (to me at any rate) friendly 'oo-oo-oo-oooooo'. This is in contrast to the chilling 'ke-wick' of the aggressive call. Most literary writers, as opposed to naturalists, describe the call as 'tu-wit to-oo'. This sound is, however, produced through the combined efforts of two birds, one providing the 'ke-wick' and the other 'oo-oo-oo'. It is thought that the 'oo-oo-oo-oooo' of the male has a triple function — it is used for announcing a claim to territory, as a courtship signal, and also as a sign to the brooding female that he has food available for collection. It is also true that the male is more of an 'oo-oooo-oo'-er and the female more of a 'kee-wit'-er. During courtship other sounds may be significant, including a hissing 'co-co-co-co-co', used mainly between males in territorial disputes. Once his territory has been successfully claimed or defended the male may change his tune to a series of soft 'oo'-ings — a very comforting sound. An angry or frightened Tawny Owl may resort to bill-snapping or a sharp 'wit-wit' call. Students of owl behaviour who venture too close to the nest would do well to heed this call as the Tawny Owl is fierce in defence of its nest. The world famous photographer Eric Hosking lost an eye in an attack by a tawny owl when he ventured too close to her nest.

As we have seen with most owls, the frequency and intensity of calls increases as the breeding season advances; this can begin as early as January and be concluded as late as July. Wet weather and strong winds have been found to reduce display activity — after all what is the point of trying to make one's voice heard over the elements. One of the early pioneers of the 'night language of *Strix*' was a Danish nightwatchman named Hansen who published his work in 1952.

Another amateur who has provided me with some salient observations on the species is a millworker from Bacup in Lancashire. Brian Oldfield noted that Tawny Owls seemed to feed their young, and indeed themselves, more often during wet and windy weather. Is this because they need more energy at this time? Probably not. On cold, calm moonlit nights, however, rodents, which are highly nutritious, can be caught partly by sight, but mostly by sound. In dark, wet, windy conditions both of these senses are less efficient, and the owl has to make do with earthworms flushed from their burrows. These are not very nutritious and therefore many more have to be eaten to maintain the basal metabolic rate. For this reason owls feed more actively on wet windy nights.

The sexes of the Tawny Owl are similar in appearance. In length it varies from 35.5-40 cm (14-16 in), with the female slightly larger than the male. The upper plumage is dark brown but liberally and attractively mottled with rusty brown, almost red in some individuals. I once watched a Tawny Owl wade into a shallow and attempt to catch tadpoles with its claws in a sheltered inlet. Several other people were also watching this bird, which was so red that from a distance they had thought it was a domestic fowl, especially as it was broad daylight. As the bird flew away, only to return later to the same spot, the light bars on the wings, formed by the buff tips on the secondary feathers, could be seen clearly.

The tail is also obviously barred. The undersurface is basically buff but striated and barred with dark brown. The feet and legs are completely feathered. The eyes are dark and lack the yellow-orange rings typical of the Long-eared Owl which is occasionally found in coniferous woodlands, a habitat sometimes used by the Tawny Owl when its preferred choice of deciduous trees is not available. The absence of ear tufts is another distinguishing feature of the Tawny Owl. It should be noted that the Tawny Owl, in addition to its division into sub-species, occurs in two distinct colour types. The rich chestnut-brown form is the one seen most often in Britain, but the lighter, greyer form does occur from time to time.

Apart from using a variety of sounds, the male

displays to the female by means of a number of subtle and surprisingly delicate body movements. He raises his wings, sways from side to side and bobs his head. The feathers are fluffed out, which substantially increases his body size. The female responds by quivering her wings. By March a nest site has been chosen, usually up to 8 m (26 ft) from the ground. Old nests of corvids are sometimes used and the dreys of grey squirrels are also taken over on occasions. I have also found nests on the ground and even under the ground, in burrows among the roots of trees. No nest material is used; the feathers which are frequently found around the site have probably been moulted naturally and not collected on purpose.

The usual clutch of eggs varies from two to six, but the average is three or four. At times when a surplus of food is available, the clutch size may be increased. The eggs measure 39 × 47 mm (1.5 × 1.9 in). The female incubates the clutch on her own, beginning with the first egg, which results in owlets of varying sizes. It is thought that each egg takes about 29 days to hatch, but because there is often a gap of a couple of days between the laying of one egg and the next, the female can be sitting for a lot longer than this.

During the whole of this period the male brings food to his mate. This is no easy task as the breeding season progresses because the female remains close to the young throughout the fledging period of up to five weeks. The male delivers the prey to a feeding station near the nest site and calls the female who then comes to collect it; in wet windy weather, however, she may prefer to continue brooding and in this case the male delivers directly to the nest site. When weather conditions are particularly bad, or when there is an above average clutch, the male may have to hunt by day as well as by night. Young Tawny owlets seem to require parental attention for up to three months after leaving the nest, but come the autumn they are chased away by the parents who are beginning to think of the following year's clutch of eggs. The dark days of autumn can echo with owl calls as the adolescents do their best to establish their own territories, as well as learning to hunt.

The diet of Tawny Owls has been worked out partly by looking at prey being brought to the nest, but mainly from the analysis of pellets which average 20 × 24 × 55 mm (0.8 × 0.9 × 2.1 in). Mammals make up a substantial part of the diet which includes shrews, voles, mice, rats and even young rabbits. Owls should therefore be welcome in large gardens and parks as they are ideal rodent controllers. They have also been known to take bats, squirrels, moles, weasels and even the occasional unfortunate kitten. Birds are also taken and almost 50 species have appeared on the owls' menu, some as large as a pheasant. In urban situations, where birds often roost in huge numbers, the owls' diet is shaped almost entirely to take advantage of this bounty. As mentioned earlier, earthworms also feature prominently in the diet. On page 00 I have discussed the possibility of owls deliberately storing surplus food; this activity has been observed in captive Tawny Owls, who also remember just where they have hidden their provisions, but despite many detailed studies of the species it is not known for certain whether this also happens in the wild. They certainly store surplus food at the nest when the young are satiated.

The main concentration of Tawny Owls is in the broadleaved forests of the boreal and temperate regions of west Eurasia. Throughout the ice ages it seems to have been resident during the interglacial periods when some degree of tree growth was possible. As woodlands reached their peak then so must the populations of *Strix aluco*, but once woodlands began to be felled these populations would have been reduced. During the nineteenth century, as shooting game birds became a favourite sport, anything with a hooked bill and talons fell foul of gamekeepers and the Tawny Owl was a frequent and gruesome sight on the keeper's gibbet. During the First World War the pressure was taken off birds of prey as the war with Germany took its toll of young sportsmen. The shortage of timber was felt during the war. At its conclusion the Forestry Commission was set up and its plantings allowed the Tawny Owl populations to recover. A series of good summers, in the period up to the mid 1950s, may also have helped. The species then suffered from the toxic chemicals used in the agriculture of the 1960s. As the Tawny Owl is not migratory, stocks cannot be replaced from overseas and recovery can be slow. Sea journeys are not undertaken and the species has still not established itself in Ireland. It is, however, Britains most common owl by far and there are thought to be between 50,000 and 100,000 pairs breeding in Britain.

Tawny Owl (*Strix aluco*)

The Spotted Owl
(*Strix occidentalis*)

This owl fills what may be loosely described as the Brown Owl's niche in the United States, although it is a larger species. Three sub-species are recognised. *Strix occidentalis caurina* occurs in the south of British Columbia to northern California but is replaced in southern California by *Strix occidentalis occidentalis*. *Strix occidentalis lucida* occurs from the south west of the USA to central Mexico.

It is around 47.5 cm (19 in) long and dark brown in colour with a smooth round head, lacking ear tufts. The eyes are large and brown, thus distinguishing it from the other large owls of the area (except for the easily recognised Barn Owl), which all have yellow or orange eyes. The heavy spotting of the undersurface of the body makes it easily recognised, but nowhere in its range is it common and in many areas it is rare.

The voice is described as a high-pitched hooting which has been compared to the barking of a small dog, and three syllables are usually clearly definable. It is usually written 'hoo-whoowhoo-hoo'. The food consists mainly of mammals but some birds and invertebrates are also taken.

The nest site is usually in a hollow tree, but the old nest of a raptor or corvid may be taken over. The Spotted Owl is said to be one of the tamest — some would say stupidest — of America's owls, a fact noted by Dickey in 1914:

'As we climbed to the young in the oak the old bird displayed her first sign of vital interest, flying within touch of the intruding heads and peering at us from close perches among the branches. But her passes at us were not fearsome things. She never even snapped her bill. Silently she swooped near, rather in an effort to see plainly, or decoy, than to harm or frighten us.'

The same observer, watching the owl at her toilet says:

'Even in the midst of her toilet there were sudden periods when Morpheus seemed to overpower her and she would doze off, only to awake with a start a few moments later and continue her performance. Her movements were much more gentle than those of the horned owls. The lack of their ear tufts and yellow irides also gave her a far more agreeable expression, although I must confess that a certain startled expression —when one did succeed in startling her — seemed unpleasantly lynx like. When she moved along a limb her every movement suggested a parrot, really a striking resemblance.'

The Barred Owl
(*Strix varia*)

This is one of America's most common large owls, being some 50 cm (20 in) long. It has a plain round head and the absence of ear tufts is typical, as are the large brown eyes. The breast is heavily cross-barred and this contrasts sharply with the longitudinally streaked abdomen. During the daytime Barred Owls retreat into the shade of the woodland, and as dark approaches they begin to call, the sound being in a higher key than that of the Great Horned Owl. The sound of *Strix varia* did not please Edward H. Forbush in 1927.

'At one of my lonely wilderness camps in the month of March a pair of Barred Owls came to the trees over my camp fire and made night hideous with their grotesque love making, banishing sleep during the evening hours. Their courting antics, as imperfectly seen by moonlight and firelight were ludicrous in the extreme. Perched in rather low branches over the fire they nodded and bowed with half-spread wings, and wobbled and twisted their heads from side to side, meantime uttering the most weird and uncouth sounds imaginable. Many of them were given with the full power of their lungs, without any regard to sleepers, whilst others were soft and cooing and more expressive of the tender emotions; sounds resembling maniacal laughter and others like mere chuckles were interspersed here and there between loud wha whas and hoo-hoo-aws'.'

Other workers have had a more generous attitude to the Barred Owl and its voice has been variously described as 'who-cooks-for-you? — who-cooks-for-you?, or eoh-who-are-you? — oh-who-are-you?' If we count the syllables we discover one of the Barred Owl's vernacular names 'the eight hooter'. At a distance the notes also sound like the barking of a dog.

The favourite habitat seems to be dense woodland clothing the banks of rivers and, given a choice, these owls prefer conifers to hardwoods. Tree cavities are the favourite nesting site, although the old nests of diurnal birds of prey or corvids may be used. The clutch size varies from two to four. The eggs are a dull white. The incubation period usually begins in February or March and starts with the first egg. The period is between 28 and 34 days. The female does most, and probably all, of the incubation but the male provides a regular supply of food. Within a week the owlets, covered in white down, have opened their eyes. They fledge after a period between seven and nine weeks. Before they fledge the owlets are agile and climb about on the branches demanding food which consists mainly of rodents. Sometimes they become too adventurous and fall to the ground, a problem also faced by young Tawny Owls. Well-meaning people may find an owlet at the base of a tree and will take the 'orphan' home in a (usually) futile attempt to rear it. If left alone, however, fallen owlets will use their bills and powerful talons to climb back up to the nest site which can be as high as 12 m (39 ft).

Five sub-species are recognised, namely *Strix varia varia* from southern Canada and east-central USA, *Strix varia georgia* from the south and south-east of America, the Texan race of *Strix varia helveola*, *Strix varia sartorii* from north and central Mexico, and *Strix varia fulvescens* from southern Mexico, western Guatemala and Honduras.

The Rusty Barred Owl
(*Strix hylophila*)

This is a monotypical species found in Brazil, Paraguay and northern Argentina.

The Rufous-legged Owl
(*Strix rufipes*)

This is another South American species which inhabits wooded valleys. So far it has been divided into three sub-species. *Strix rufipes chacoensis* comes from Paraguay and northern Argentina, *Strix rufipes sonbom* comes from Chiloe Island, off Argentina, while the race from southern Chile and southern Argentina is *Strix rufipes rufipes*.

The Ural Owl
(*Strix uralensis*)

This well documented species is divided into ten sub-species (see Table 28). This is a light brown owl which is very similar to, but much larger than, the Tawny Owl. The Ural Owl is 59 cm (23 in) long and has a massive wingspan of around 1.2 m (4 ft). On average the female is larger than the male, but the plumage of the two is alike. They are greyish-brown, but heavily striated with dark brown, especially on the undersurface. The flight feathers and the long tail have a buff ground colour transversed by bands of brown and tipped with white. The head is round and the brown eyes are surprisingly small for a *Strix* owl. The greyish-white facial disc is almost devoid of markings, which distinguishes the Ural Owl from the Great Grey Owl which has many lines on its facial disc.

Ural Owls show a preference for mixed or coniferous forests, but in recent years the species has accepted nest boxes. In Rumania breeding has occurred up to heights of 1,600 m (5,200 ft). They do, however, find very dense woodlands unacceptable, although this may be due to the lack of open spaces across which to hunt. Mammals form a substantial proportion of the diet, with voles and mice being the main prey. They also take squirrels, hedgehogs, hares and the occasional weasel (*Mustella nivalis*). The thick powerful talons are capable of killing surprisingly large prey, including birds as large as the hazel hen (*Tetrastes bonasia*), black grouse (*Lyrurus tetrix*) and partridge (*Perdix perdix*), while a variety of small birds are also taken, including crows, wood-peckers, pigeons, thrushes and finches. Fish are often taken, as are frogs and a wide variety of insects. The species hunts mainly at night, but there are times during the breeding season when the male has to hunt during the day also, to provide food for the female and the growing owlets.

At the onset of the breeding season the Ural Owl becomes extremely vocal. The male calls 'hu-ooo hu-ooo hu-hoo-hoo' to advertise his occupancy of a territory, to which the female replies with a harsh croaking 'vchä-vchä-hävähä'. The male also has a 'wowowowowo' alarm call.

The nest site is usually in a tree stump, a hole, the old nest of a raptor or corvid, or perhaps even in the drey of a squirrel. The weather does seem to have some bearing upon egg-laying, which begins soon after the snow has melted. In northern Europe this might be as late as mid-May, while it will usually be somewhat earlier in the south. The clutch size varies from two to seven but is more usually three. There may be an interval of several days between the laying of successive eggs. Each egg is incubated by the female alone for 28 days, during which time she is provided with food by the male. Despite the size of the clutch, it is most unusual for more than two owlets to reach fledging stage.

The fledging period is around 40 days although most young have left the nest before this to go scrambling about among the foliage. It may be some three or four months before they are independent of their parents. While some precocious Ural Owls may breed in the year following their birth, this is the exception rather than the rule and many probably do not breed until they are three or even four years old.

Many species of owl have suffered the loss of their habitat because of human activities. In the case of the Ural Owl, however, human enterprises have been beneficial. This owl has adapted to life in newly planted forests as well as accepting the close proximity of buildings and the provision of nest boxes.

David's Wood Owl
(*Strix davidi*)

This is one of the rarest of the world's birds. There is only one tiny population in China, which, at the time of writing has not yet been studied.

The Great Grey Owl
(*Strix nubulosa*)

In contrast to David's Wood Owl this is one of the world's most studied owls. It is divided into three subspecies. *Strix nebulosa nebulosa* is from North America, *Strix nubulosa lapponica* occurs in northern Europe, northern Asia and the island of Sakhalin, and *Strix nebulosa elisabethae* is the race found in northern Mongolia. It has never been recorded in Britain.

This is one of the largest owls in the world, being between 64 and 76 cm (25-30 in) long — the females being larger on average than the males. To some degree the long tail of the species make it appear larger than it actually is; it is quite light compared to the Eagle Owl and is not as powerful as one might imagine.

The long tail and heavy round head give the Great Grey Owl an appearance unlike any other owl, especially in flight. Its plumage is white, grey and brown. The uppersurface is irregularly marked with deep brown and white, while beneath there is bold streaking superimposed over fine barring. The facial disc is basically white but with several concentric circles of brown. Small yellow eyes peep out from these discs and another prominent facial feature is a black beard-like marking around the bill. There are also white moustache-like marks and an obvious series of white patches on the central area of the foreneck.

The diet consists mainly of small voles. In Europe there are records of the Water Vole (*Arvicola terrestris*) being taken, and small birds are also hunted. In America voles, mice and a few larger mammals, including squirrels, are taken, but here very few birds seem to be killed by Great Grey Owls. The pellets average $25 \times 30 \times 63$ mm ($1 \times 1.2 \times 2.5$ in) and are produced at the daytime roost. This is usually situated in dense coniferous forest close to open moorland over which hunting can take place. Many Great Grey Owls are resident, but in the northerly part of the range they may be nomadic, especially in winter when the regular food supply fails. As the breeding season approaches, the male develops his long-drawn-out call, consisting of four syllables, the female responding with a shorter and more highly pitched call. The calls are weaker than might be expected from such a large bird. Bill-snapping is also a feature of the display.

The nest site is usually in a pine tree in which there is to be found an old nest of another bird of prey, such as an Osprey or a Buzzard. The Great Grey Owl is said to line the nest with pine needles or strips of bark. Some workers have suggested that this species sometimes constructs a platform of twigs. Surprisingly for an owl, there are no records of nests in tree cavities. This might be due to the fact that the owl's eyes are so small that they would not function too well in the dim recesses of a hole. This may also be why this owl is often seen hunting in daylight, although its hearing is remarkably good.

The clutch size varies from two to nine, the actual number varying according to the abundance or otherwise of the vole population. There is an interval of between two and four days, occasionally even longer, between the laying of one egg and the next. The eggs are ovoid rather than round, which may well be an adaptation to the fact of the nest being more exposed than that of most other owl species. The average size of the white, slightly glossy eggs is 43 × 53 mm (1.7 × 2 in). Both male and female defend the nest site with great, and often frightening ferocity.

Only the female incubates the eggs and she begins with the first egg, resulting in a synchronomous hatching. During the 28—30-day period the female is fed by the male and this feeding continues as the female broods the young for the first fourteen days after hatching. The fledging period is between 60 and 65 days. Both parents are kept busy feeding them for up to 150 days, after which the owlets are independent. They are occasionally able to breed the following year, but it is more usual for them to breed at the age of two.

This concludes a survey of the *Strix* owls. Before ending this chapter, however, we must consider one more genus.

GENUS
RHINOPTYNX

Only the Striped Owl (*Rhinoptynx clamator*) occurs in this genus. It is divided into three sub-species. These are *Rhinoptynx clamator clamator* from south-east Mexico, *Rhinoptynx clamator oberi* from the Tobago Islands, and *Rhinoptynx clamator midas* from southern Brazil, Paraguay, Uruguay and northern Argentina.

This is a medium-sized owl, measuring between 32.5 and 37.5 cm (13-15 in), which has prominent, almost black ear tufts. The iris of the eye is light brown to orange-yellow. The upper surface is brownish-buff, with the pale facial disc edged round with black. The undersurface is very pale but heavily streaked with dark brown.

Its preferred habitat is around open grassy areas and shrubby clearings, the bird resting in the trees, although apparently it nests on the ground. The voice is described as a penetrating semi-whistled 'wheeeyoo' and a series of barking hoots 'ow-ow-ow-ow' (P. Schwartz). It feeds on mammals, but very little is known of its breeding biology.

Long-eared Owl

photographed by Michael Edwards

CHAPTER ELEVEN

The Asio, Pseudoscops, Nesasio and Aegolius Owls

This collection of twelve attractive species all belong to the sub-family Striginae.

The Long-eared Owl
(*Asio otus*)

This owl is more migratory than many other species. I had this fact proved to me in November 1984 at the South Walney Bird Reserve in Cumbria. I was helping to drive a number of small birds, particularly Greenfinches (*Carduelis chloris*), into a Heligoland trap. This trap is shaped like a funnel and fringed with bushes to attract passerines. The birds feeding in these bushes are flushed by the clapping of hands and then driven into the trap which gets narrower and narrower until it ends in a catching box. The wide end is sealed by springing a trap door after the birds have entered. On this momentous occasion a storm had just abated and the bushes were full of birds feeding and resting. Suddenly the trap was full of frightened birds although none of the human operators was anywhere near. By the time we reached the catching box it was full of greenfinch feathers and two very self-satisfied-looking Long-eared Owls. The ringers discovered the extent of the owls' ferocity as they measured, weighed and released them.

The average size is around 35.5 cm (14 in), with the female being slightly larger then the male; the average weight is around 300 g (just over 11 oz), but this varies a lot depending upon season and food supply.

The uppersurface is buff-brown richly covered with streaks of brown and patches of white and buff which combine to produce a delightfully marbled effect. Handling the two Long-eared Owls on Walney enabled me to see this patterning in daylight, but this hardly gives a clue as to its real function. As the owls' daytime roosts are in conifer plantations this mottled pattern provides a perfect camouflage among the trees through which sunshine floods to create a similar dappled shadowing.

The roost on Walney often consisted of as many as eight birds, and communal roosting does seem to be more of a feature of this species than other owls — this may well be due to the fact that they are more migratory and are used to sticking together during these journeys. Their long wings are more pointed than is usual in owls, which makes them strong fliers — while in the air the careful observer will see a dark carpal patch standing out against the paler undersurface of the wings.

The head, especially when the ear tufts are up, is surprisingly cat-like. The facial disc is browny-buff with black patches close to the fierce-looking orange eyes. The ear tufts can be held flat but are extended if the bird is angry or worried, and it might be that they help to break up the body pattern and, in the depths of a tree's shade, may even look quite 'branch-like'.

The upper surface of the tail is buff-coloured, but strongly marked by six to eight dark brown bars. The undersurface is buff, but with brownish longitudinal stripes which work wonderfully well as camouflage. The observer looking upwards into the light finds great difficulty in unravelling this dappled image and spotting an owl. The body colour does vary a great deal and some workers feel that it is related to geographical distribution. This may be true for the American sub-species *Asio otus wilsonianus* which has a red-brown facial disc. On the whole, however, it is thought that colour varies more according to age and sex.

Altogether there are four sub-species. *Asio otus otus* occurs in Europe, Asia and north-west Africa, *Asio otus tufsi* in northern Canada, while *Asio otus wilsonianus* occurs in southern Canada and in west and central America. This leaves the Canary Islands race, which is named *Asio otus canariensis*.

The diet will obviously vary with geographical location and my own studies indicate a high proportion of mammals, especially Short-tailed Field Voles (*Microtus agrestis*). At a Lancashire roost I found 73 per cent of the items in the pellets were from this species, plus a further 20 per cent of Long-tailed Field Mouse (*Apodemus sylvaticus*). In Ireland, however, the Short-tailed Field Vole does not occur and here we find a greater dependence upon Brown Rats (*Rattus norvegicus*).

Birds do occur in the diet, with crows, hirundines, thrushes, titmice, and some starlings all being taken. In Britain House Sparrows (*Passer domesticus*) are taken but this does not seem to be the case in other parts of the range. Most owls will take shrews, but it is regarded as very unusual for the Long-eared Owl to do so. It could be that this species has a sense of taste, for it is known that shrews taste bitter; while domestic cats will kill shrews, they will not eat them. (Some people will feel I am being fanciful in thinking that an owl could have a sense of taste, but it is not so long ago that we thought no birds had a sense of smell and we now know that this is incorrect.)

A lot of work has been done on the senses and hunting techniques of Long-eared Owls. It is known that their powers of hearing are such that on still nights they can catch prey in total darkness. There are also records of them hunting in pairs during dusk and dawn, one flying along a hedgerow, the other flying slightly behind on the opposite side and pouncing on small birds which are flushed out. This is likely to be a winter occupation only. During the breeding season the male has to provide food for his mate while she is incubating eggs or brooding young.

As one would expect with a nocturnal species, the Long-eared Owl is very vocal. Calling begins about a month before egg-laying and one 'song' consists of three short calls which, in the United States, have been likened to the call of the Mourning Dove (*Zenaida macroura*). The sound has also been compared to someone blowing across the neck of an empty bottle. There is also an acrobatic display flight, during which the male produces impressively long wing-claps. In 1966 Hawley described the Long-eared Owl's vocabulary as 'remarkable' and work done since this time only serves to reinforce his opinion. The male's territorial call may be written 'hoo-hoo-hoo', with the female replying 'shoo-oogh'. There are also hissing calls which sound very cat-like; apparently this is used when the male delivers food to the female, but I have never heard this myself. I have, however, frequently been subjected to a barking 'woof-woof' followed by a 'woo-ack woo-ack' whenever I have approached too close to a nest or roosting site.

The nest site chosen is usually an old nest of a corvid or a diurnal bird of prey, but there are also ground nests in some of the northerly parts of its range where suitable trees might be at a premium. Some ornithologists have suggested that the owls may also take over the drey of a squirrel and actually carry out repairs; fewer workers have suggested that Long-eared Owls may build a nest from scratch.

In Britain egg-laying usually begins in April but it may be later than this in the colder areas of northern Europe where the snow lies longer. The clutch size has been found to vary with the availability of food and, as with the Snowy Owl, gluts of rodents result in big clutches. At these times the Long-eared Owl may lay as many as ten eggs and even second broods are produced, but the average clutch is four or five. The white, glossy eggs are almost spherical and measure 33 × 40 mm (1.3 × 1.6 in). The female begins incubation with the laying of the first egg and each one takes between 26 and 30 days to hatch. It has been suggested that the male may occasionally sit on the eggs, but this is not a usual event and more work needs to be done on the species before we can be certain. What is certain is that the male provides the food, although despite his efforts, not all the owlets survive. At hatching the young are a swan-like white but this is soon replaced by grey down with untidy-looking brown quill feathers poking through, making the owlets look like little round hedgehogs.

The owlets leave the nest after 23 days but it may be a further fortnight before they can fly with any degree of competence. They become independent after a further month and probably breed the following season.

Long-eared Owl *(Asio otus)*

The status of the Long-eared Owl in Britain is interesting, the population being somewhere between 10,000 and 50,000 breeding pairs. This lack of precision with regard to population may be attributed to this owl's furtive habits. The species appears not to be able to compete with the heavier and perhaps more aggressive Tawny Owl, which pushes it out of deciduous woodlands or even kills it. This may be why the Long-eared Owl has taken to conifer plantations, which Tawny Owls tend not to like. In Ireland, where the Tawny Owl does not exist, the Long-eared Owl seems quite happy in deciduous and mixed woodlands.

The Stygian Owl
(*Asio stygius*)

This owl is not very well recorded, but is a similar species to the Long-eared Owl. It is separated into six sub-species. *Asio stygius stygius* is found in Brazil, *Asio stygius lambi* in north-west Mexico, *Asio stygius robustus* in east Mexico, Guatemala and Nicaragua, *Asio stygius siguapa* in Cuba and the Isle of Pines, *Asio stygius barboroi* in Paraguay and northern Argentina, *Asio stygius noctipetens* in the West Indies islands of Gonave and Hispaniola.

The Abyssinian Long-eared Owl
(*Asio abyssinicus*)

This owl has been considered as conspecific with *Asio otus*, but the more recent view is to consider it as the African Long-eared Owl, found in open areas of grassland and ravines. Two sub-species have been recognised. The Ethiopian race is *Asio abyssinicus abyssinicus*, while that from Mount Kenya and eastern Zaire has been designated *Asio abyssinicus graueri*.

The Madagascar Long-eared Owl
(*Asio madagascariensis*)

There has been very little study of this owl. As its name implies, it is restricted to the island of Madagascar.

The Short-eared Owl
(*Asio flammeus*)

'There suddenly appeared a multitude of mice which overwhelmed the marshes, shearing and gnawing the grass and so spoiling and tainting it that the cattle grazing it were smitten with a murrain and died. Man could not destroy them but finally more owls than could have existed in the whole country flocked to the marshes and so the marsh-holders were delivered from their plague of mice.'

This Pied Piper-type story was documented by Hollinshed in his *Chronicles of England, Scotland and Ireland*. He is describing a plague of what we can assume were Short-tailed Field Voles (*Microtus agrestis*) in the Southminster marshes of Essex in 1580. The owls so praised must have been Short-eared Owls and I have seen 'shorties' deal with similar smaller, but still impressive plagues on salt marshes in Scotland and Cumbria. The species has an almost worldwide distribution and is divided into the ten sub-species summarised in Table 29.

The ear tufts of the Short-eared Owl are so short that they are usually invisible, and as if this were not confusing enough, the specific name of *flammeus*, meaning 'flame-coloured', is even more misleading. The colour is certainly nothing like a flame, but is an attractive pattern of mottled brown which earned the bird its Old English name of Woodcock Owl. It has been suggested that the Woodcock (*Scolopax rusticola*) and Short-eared Owl arrive together on migration, but I wonder if this is an error in identification caused because they are so very similar in plumage.

The uppersurface is a subtle mixture of buff and dark brown, while the long wings are tipped with black above. When viewed from below dark bars are clearly visible on the wings but less so on the uppersurface. The trailing edge to the wing is yellowish. The lemon-coloured eyes are in contrast to the fierce orange irises of the Long-eared Owl. The facial disc of the Short-eared Owl is pale but quite dark in the region of the eyes. Both the bill, except for a pale tip, and the claws are black and the legs are fully feathered. The undersurface is pale buff which, in flight, gives the bird a very light appearance, although it is not as pale as the Barn Owl (*Tyto alba*).

Short-eared Owls, especially in their wintering grounds which are often on or around salt marshes, are at times quite diurnal in their habits. They also tend to roost in grass cover on sloping ground overlooking a suitable hunting ground which they slowly quarter, and are therefore sometimes confused with harriers. Although they will take birds such as waders, gulls and passerines, the bulk of the diet consists of mammals. In Britain Short-tailed Field Voles, Bank Voles and occasionally, rats, mice and rabbits are taken along with the occasional squirrel.

The pellet size averages about $19 \times 23 \times 49$ mm ($0.7 \times 0.9 \times 1.9$ in) and of 100 pellets I analysed from a Lancashire moorland, the food seemed to be around 95 per cent mammal, although there was some evidence that the odd bird might have pounced on a meadow pipit. I found no evidence of game chicks being taken, even although grouse were raised on the same moor. The work of Erkinaro (1973) has shown that there is a seasonal variation in pellet size, those in spring and autumn being larger than the summer and winter pellets. Why this should be so has not been satisfactorily explained. One possible reason may be that the pellets are never easy to find. My 100 pellets from Lancashire were gathered at a communal roost used by between six and eight birds during early autumn.

Breeding over most of the range takes place on open moorland, but in Finland nests have been found in forest clearings, while newly planted areas or regions of scrubland are sometimes selected in both Britain and America. Nests can be single or in loose colonies and the build-up to copulation and egg-laying can be one of the most exciting events in a birdwatcher's calendar.

Spectacular acrobatic courtship flights involve loud wing-clapping, tumbling falls and quavering chattering cries which echo over the moors. Although the male takes the leading role, the female, too, enjoys the occasional 'flutter'. The male also hovers like a kestrel in the wind and produces a haunting 'voo-hoo-hoo-hoo-hoo' lasting for three or four seconds. A female, suitably, impressed, perches on a post, wall or shrub and calls 'keee-yow' to show her readiness to accept the breeding area and the male who goes with it. Once established, the pair defend territory, eggs and chicks with great ferocity against human intruders, but particularly against crows and gulls which will take both eggs and small owlets. A barking call is reserved for intruders. I once made the mistake of ignoring this warning and received a smart bang on the back of the neck as a reward for my stupidity.

The nest is almost always on the ground, usually hidden, but it can sometimes be suprisingly exposed. Occasionally it is lined with vegetation. The clutch size varies from four to ten, the large clutches reflecting a glut of rodents. During a really prolific vole year, breeding can begin as early as March and two clutches may be produced. Eggs are usually laid at two-day intervals, resulting in a group of owlets of varying sizes. Not all are reared. The size of the egg averages 30×40 mm (1.2×1.6 in). In the initial stages the female, who does all the work, does not sit very closely and so early eggs may have a longer incubation period. In Canada it has been suggested that the male shares in incubation. The average, and in this instance one should stress 'average', incubation period per egg is 27-30 days.

Newly hatched chicks are covered in white down and their eyes do not open for about a week; sometimes the shafts of the down feathers are grey and this can make the owlets look a little grubby. Because of the difference in size, the strongest often eat the weakest. They leave the nest long before they can fly, often as young as 14 days and then they wander about demanding food from the parents until they fly at the age of about 27 days. These young owls have a prominent patch of white feathers close to the bill, which the parents seem to use as a 'target' when feeding them.

The Marsh Owl
(*Asio capensis*)

This is another species in which the female is larger than the male, the average size being between 29 and 31.5 cm ($11\frac{1}{2}$-$12\frac{1}{2}$ in). It is divided into three sub-species. *Asio capensis capensis* ranges from Ethiopia to Angola and Cape Province, and *Asio capensis tingitanus* occurs in north-west Africa and from Senegal to Cameroon. *Asio capensis hova* is the race confined to Madagascar.

The main coloration is a dullish brown on the uppersurface. This seems to serve to accentuate the effect of the huge dark brown eyes which gaze in a surprised, and some say rather sad-looking, manner out of the paler facial disc which is framed in black. The flight feathers are very dark brown and the tail feathers are also dark in the centre; the outer feathers are buff-coloured but with a number of dark bars. The under-

Short-eared Owl (*Asio flammeus*)

surface is very pale buff and although there are spots and bars, the contrast between the dorsal and ventral surfaces is very marked. The legs and feet are well covered by white feathers. In flight the underwing shows a pale patch at the base of the primaries and on the tips of the greater coverts. The wing tips are black and there is also a dark patch in the carpal (wrist) region. The flight is graceful and bouyant, the hunting technique being surprisingly harrier-like. In areas where the range overlaps with that of the Short-eared Owl, the two can be distinguished by the fact that the Marsh Owl is smaller and has an unstreaked chest which enables easy idenification.

The prey of the Marsh Owl consists mainly of mammals. In South Africa Dr. Mendlesohn has noted that Multimammate Mice account for around 80 per cent of the birds' diet, but that other rodents, birds, insects, frogs and lizards are also eaten. The favoured habitat is long grass surrounding lowland swamps, the nest being sited in tall grass, in an old corvid's nest or in a short burrow. Vocalisations increase prior to the breeding season which can begin as early as February. A deep 'kaaa', sounding distinctly frog-like, is produced either in flight or on the ground. During an impressive display flight 'kaa-kaa-kaa-kaa-aa-aa' is called in quick succession and the sound is like the call of a duck. During the flight the pair fly around in wide circles on slow, very deliberate wing beats.

Eggs are usually present in the nest from the end of February in some areas but can be as late as May in others. The clutch size is around three, laid at two-day intervals, each egg being white, slightly glossy and of an average size of 34 × 40 mm (1.3 × 1.6 in). Usually only one brood is raised but on rare occasions, when there is a glut of mammals, a second brood may at least be attempted. The incubation period is around 28 days, beginning with the first egg, and it is thought that the male may assist the female. After about 20 days the owlets leave the nest, although both parents continue to feed the young for a further month or so before they become independent. It is probable that the Marsh Owl is able to breed during its first year of life.

GENUS
PSEUDOSCOPS

The Jamaican Owl (*Pseudoscops grammicus*) is found only in Jamaica.

GENUS
NESASIO

The Fearful Owl (*Nesasio solomonensis*) is found on the islands of Bougainville, Chorseul and Ysabel.

GENUS
AEGOLIUS

Four species make up this genus.

Tengmalm's Owl
(*Aegolius funereus*)

This is a widely distributed species which has been divided into eight sub-species (see Table 30).

Despite being only about 25 cm (10 in) long, this delightful little brownish owl is able to cope with the cool climate of northern and central Europe where it inhabits coniferous forests. It also fills the same niche in North America. The large round head and prominent facial disc make the species easily identifiable, as do the large yellow eyes. There is also a set of what look like raised white eyebrows, which give it a somewhat startled expression. The upperparts are basically dark brown but are covered with numerous spots. The undersurface is paler, but also blotched with brown. The vernacular name derives from Peter Gustavus Tengmalm, a Swedish ornithologist who classified this bird in 1783. Its name in Swedish is *parluggla*, which means the 'pearly owl', a clear reference to the white markings on its plumage. The scientific name for this owl, *Aegolius funereus* means 'the owl of ill-omen'. In Canada and America the species is known as the Boreal Owl and the New World has its own folklore connected with the species as recorded by the Montagnais Indians in southern Labrador:

'Once upon a time the largest owl in the world, who was very proud of his great voice, tried to imitate the voice of the waterfall and to drown out its roar. But the impertinence of this ambition so angered the Great Spirit that he humiliated the huge bird by transforming him to a pygmy and changing his voice to the feeble notes which resemble the slow dripping of water.'

The species has also been known as Richardson's Owl.

Tengmalm's Owl *(Aegolius funereus) — juvenile*

supply of food. The fledging period is about 32 days; independence is reached after about six weeks and breeding occurs in the year following the owlet's birth.

When it is not hunting, Tengmalm's Owl tends to remain absolutely still, pressed hard up against the bark of a tree. The mottled brown-and-white plumage provides perfect camouflage.

To describe this owl as blind or stupid, as some have done, is clearly wrong on both counts. What is true is that this little owl is perfectly adapted to its environment, and the New World name of Boreal Owl is probably ideal for it.

It is often stated that this species is diurnal, but it hardly has any option in this because in the northerly latitudes there may be almost 24 hours of daylight. The diet consists mainly of small mammals, particularly voles and lemmings, but small birds also often form a substantial part of the food of this species in some areas. It does seem, however, that these owls prefer mammals providing a ready supply is available.

As the breeding season approaches vocalisation increases and what was only a 'dripping of water' now almost becomes a flood. Three to six 'poo poo poo poo' calls are produced by the male, usually from a perch, but he also calls while in flight, at which time he tends to accelerate the notes into a high-pitched trill. There is also an alarm call, 'kop-kop-kop', issued when danger threatens the nest. This is usually to be found in a nest hole, often one previously used by a woodpecker.

In America symbolic feeding has been described as part of the courtship cycle, the male calling and also enticing the female into the nest hole with a rodent. Wing-clapping has also been observed. The clutch size varies from three to seven and even up to ten when food is plentiful. The white eggs are smooth and glossy and average 27 × 33 mm (1 × 1.3 in) in size. The incubation period is around 28 days and is usually done by the female on her own, apparently beginning with the second egg. Thus we have asynchronous hatching to produce owlets of different sizes, which are brooded more or less continuously by the female for 22 days. During all of this period the male provides a steady

The Saw-whet Owl
(*Aegolius acadius*)

This exists as two sub-species. *Aegolius acadius acadius* occurs in Canada, western USA and northern Mexico, while *Aegolius acadius brooksi* is restricted to Queen Charlotte Island, USA.

Several vernacular names have been applied to this owl. Saw-whet obviously refers to the sound of a mill saw being sharpened on a whetstone, and old timers working the mills must have noticed the similarity of the owls' call. The Acadian Owl was another of its old names, referring to the place of its initial discovery. The Sparrow Owl refers to its diminutive size (about 20 cm/8 in), as does yet another name — the Mouse Owl. The Saw-filer is self-explanatory. La Petite Nyctale, the French Canadian name, means the 'little night owl', while the White-fronted Owl refers to the pale streaking on its facial disc. There are no ear tufts and the Saw-whet can be further distinguished from the Pygmy Owl by its pale undersurface crossed by soft brown stripes, its proportionally large head and shorter tail.

At one time young Saw-whets were thought to be a completely different species, those making this decision usually working from museum skins rather than field observations. Young Saw-whets are chocolate-brown with a blackish face and conspicuous white patches or 'eyebrows' forming a V between the eyes. At roost the species is quite prepared to rely on camouflage and is thus often described as ridiculously tame, as was reported by Austing, writing in the *Audubon* magazine in 1858.

'I have been within a few feet of the one without seeing it. And then, suddenly, I found myself face to face with the little sprite. . . I have often reached up casually and plucked the unsuspecting owl from its perch.'

Unlike well-behaved Victorian children this 'little sprite' is more often heard than seen. A rapidly produced 'woo-ik, woo-ik, woo-ik' is the male's most common call and it is repeated with almost monotonous regularity. The saw-like 'skreigh-aw skreigh-aw' is less regular but, when produced, is the most diagnostic call of the species. It can also rasp, whistle, squeak and give a fair imitation of a bell. Calling increases in regularity and complexity as the breeding season gets underway in February.

After almost a century of doubt, it is now established that Saw-whets migrate in some numbers, moving south through the woodlands and southern Canada, the United States and even into western Mexico. During this movement residents meet migrants and challenge each other. Eventually territory is established in swampy areas surrounded by coniferous forests, but alder thickets, cedar groves and tamarask bogs are also suitable habitats. A woodpecker hole is usually the choice of nest site, especially if it is between 5-15 m (16-49 ft) high.

The clutch size varies from four to seven, and the female begins her incubation stint with the laying of the first egg. Each dull white egg takes around 27 days to hatch, but because there can be a gap of two or three days between the laying of one egg and the next, the owlets can show considerable variation in size. The male is kept very busy providing mice, frogs and birds for his ever-hungry dependants. The young are fledged in just over a month, but the parents remain in attendance until well into the summer, after which the young lose their distinctive juvenile plumage. In view of this long period of care, it is surprising to find some workers suggesting that the Saw-whet might be double-brooded. If this is a regular occurrence, then there must be a good number of tired owls resting in the North American woodlands during the fall!

The Unspotted Saw-whet or Central American Saw-whet Owl
(*Aegolius ridgwayi*)

This is divided into three sub-species. *Aegolius ridgwayi tacanensis* is from southern Mexico, *Aegolius ridgwayi rostratus* from Guatemala, and *Aegolius ridgwayi ridgwayi* from Costa Rica.

About 18 cm (7 in) long, this rare owl frequents upland forests. It is dark brown above, including the face, but with a contrasting white forehead and narrow line over the eye. It is buff below with an indistinct cinnamon band across the breast. It shows a striking resemblance to the juvenile Saw-whet Owl described above. Very little is known of its biology or habits but the Costa Rican sub-species is reported as producing a longish series of rhythmic whistles of equal pitch.

The Buff-fronted Owl
(*Aegolius harrisii*)

This owl is not documented, but from museum specimens it has been divided into two sub-species. *Aegolius harrisii harrisii* comes from Colombia, Ecuador and Venezuela, and *Aegolius harrisii iheringi* from south-east Brazil, Paraguay and northern Argentina.

Turkestan Eagle Owl (*Bubo b. turcomanus*)*See page 48*

CHAPTER TWELVE

Owl Conservation

One of the most overused words of the latter half of the twentieth century is without doubt 'conservation'. It is used as if it were a magic word — all we have to do is utter it in the right context and our fauna and flora are safe. How, for example, does one set about conserving a bird? It is clearly impossible in isolation. We need to do two things. First, the habitat in which the species lives should be preserved. The forest or the moorland should not be exploited at the expense of the bird. Second, potentially hazardous pollutants should not be sprayed directly upon the habitat or allowed to drift in on the wind or on the current of a stream or river. These aims would be easily accomplished except for one, often insurmountable factor — money! Try telling a starving man not to harvest the timber of a forest to provide his family with food, in order to preserve a rare owl and see what answer you get.

Another factor which conservationists fail to take into account is climatic change which can affect the distribution of a species. If the climate of the north lands became tropical, there could be no place there for the Snowy Owl and we would be quite wrong to grieve its passing. The Eagle Owl does not breed in Britain because the habitat is not suitable. We should not, therefore, worry. The Eagle Owl does, however, breed in Norway and is decreasing there — this *ought* to worry us and some consideration should be given as to how to deal with this type of problem.

Compared to many parts of the world, such as South America and Madagascar, for example, Europe has been most fortunate in that it lost only two of its bird species in recent centuries; the Bald Ibis (*Geronticus calvus*) still survives in North Africa, but has now gone from Europe, while the Great Auk (*Pinguinus impennis*), with its sweet-tasting flesh, is now extinct altogether.

None of the European owls is extinct, although both the Snowy and the Eagle Owl are giving cause for concern in some areas. Birds of prey are in particular danger, mainly because of people's ambivalent attitude towards them. On the one hand, we respect their power and hunting ability, and yet we worry about them practising their lethal skill on our livestock, reared for food or especially for sport. The increasing efficiency of firearms has resulted in almost two centuries of unrelenting slaughter. Added to a loss of habitat due to tree felling and the increased use of persistent pesticides, this leads up to a massive reduction in many owl populations.

Let us first consider the pesticide problem because in many ways this is the easiest problem to rectify providing we allow the time and, above all, the money.

DDT

The first chemical to be used in quantity in the agricultural industry was dichlorodiphenyltrichoroethane, better known as DDT, which was first synthesised in 1874. It was not until 1939, however, that its devastating effect on insects was discovered. It was, quite rightly to begin with, welcomed as a 'miracle insecticide' as it killed the malaria-carrying mosquito and the louse which transmitted typhus, and must thus have saved millions of human lives. What was not foreseen was the effect the chemical had on other forms of wildlife and it is a perfect, although tragic, example of the need for field-testing new chemicals.

In America it was used against Pine-looper caterpillars and the Dutch Elm Beetle, saving millions of dollars of landowners' and shareholders' money. It was only later — much later — that DDT was discovered to have an adverse effect on the breeding of large birds of prey, whose populations declined almost to extinction without the reason being immediately apparent. In 1972 DDT was banned in North America, but it is still used freely in other parts of the world, especially in underdeveloped countries with an insect pest problem.

The real danger of DDT, to human as well as animal life, is its persistence in the food chain. Let us see how the Barn Owl was affected. In order to kill insect pests the grain fields were sprayed with DDT. The insects were killed but many, on the verge of dying, were eaten by shrews, while voles and mice picked up contaminated vegetation. The owls then ate the mammals as well as small birds which had also fed on the insects and vegetable matter.

If administered in small enough doses, it was thought that while DDT would kill tiny insects, it was too weak to affect animals, especially those as large as humans. What was overlooked, however, was that the chemical does not pass through the body but is actually soluble in the body fat. Even this is safe so long as this body fat is left in storage. But let us look at our owl on a freezing cold night when food is hard to find. It has to draw upon its reserves of fat and this releases the poison into its blood stream at the very time when the owl is at its weakest.

Could these dead owls be replaced in the summer by an above-average breeding season? The answer, unfortunately, is no, because it has been discovered that DDT interferes with the production of the sex hormones, particularly oestrogen. Low levels of oestrogen adversely affect the movement of the calcium within the body, which is essential for eggshell formation. Mainly as a result of the work of Dr Derek Ratcliffe of Monks Wood Research Station in England, owl eggshells were proved to have become much thinner in the period during which DDT was used. As the adult owl (or any other bird species affected) settled on the eggs to begin incubation, they collapsed under its weight. In the 1960s many birds of prey were accused by naturalists of having developed cannibalistic tendencies because they were eating their own eggs. This accusation was made in the light of observation without any other more scientific explanation. The incubating bird recognised the whole egg, which evoked the response of incubating, while a broken egg was not recognised as such and was eaten.

PCB

Such was the apparent success of DDT in the early years of its use that the elated biochemists set about finding new and better insecticides. The DDT-related aldrin and dieldrin were even better killers and were used liberally in the 1960s, with catastrophic side effects. These were then labelled as environmentally bad and were replaced by poly-chlorinated-biphenyls, which are said to have been responsible for the deaths of 10,000 seabirds in the Irish Sea. Other nations using PCBs have similar horror stories to tell.

Clearly the world has to be fed, so we must ask the questions: 'Can we have our cake and eat it safely?' The qualified answer would seem to be yes, but any chemical used in the environment must satisfy the following points. First, the chemical should be a 'specific' killer, destroying the targeted pest, but causing little damage to useful species and to the vertebrate animals. Any herbicide or insecticide which affects the fabric of the ecosystem should be banned. Obviously this involves rigorous field-testing and puts up the price of the chemical.

Second, the chemical should be easy to apply and must either stay where it is put or decay quickly after its work is done. There can be no excuse for chemicals which dissolve in water and then become concentrated when the sun's heat evaporates the water, to leave behind the lethal substance.

Finally, no chemical should be applied to large areas without sufficient reason and, perhaps more contentiously, without a specific warrant.

Mercury

As an alternative to the DDT and PCBs mainly used in North America and Britain, some countries, particularly Sweden, have used compounds of mercury both as a seed dressing and as part of the process of pulping wood. Mercury is also difficult to eliminate from the body and, even worse, it tends to concentrate in the brain cells and cause irreparable damage. Mercury and lead salts were once used in curing pelts for the hat-making industries thoughout Europe. These salts were absorbed through the skin and damaged the brain cells of the workers — by the time an apprentice had completed his training he was often 'as mad as a hatter'.

It is now known that due to a gradual build-up of mercury salts in the brain, the populations of Swedish predatory birds fell alarmingly. It was discovered that some mercury also became incorporated into the feathers of Sea Eagles and, more important in the context of this book, of Eagle Owls. Scientists have been able to compare the mercury levels of feathers from museum specimens, birds found dead when the effect was first noticed to be killing birds in the 1960s, and present-day Eagle Owls. Thus the owl is being used as a pollution indicator.

What affects birds today may well be our problem tomorrow. The cynical among us can perhaps be excused for believing that a bird which is so useful in monitoring our own environment is more likely to be conserved!

Loss of Habitat

The effect of herbicides and insecticides has had one more disastrous effect upon wildlife — they have simply been too efficient. Because of the excess food produced by fewer workers, countryfolk seeking jobs have moved to the cities. The increasing population demands more and bigger houses, more parks, more roads, railways and airports, all of which eat up acres of land. The invention of huge labour-saving machinery meant that fields were too small, so down came the hedgerows. The general twentieth-century population is better educated and reads more books and periodicals. We need paper to print these on and so we are now eating into the world's woodlands at an alarming rate. It is easy to decide to replant these woodlands in the future, but by that time many rare species of birds, including owls, will have been lost for ever. Not all owls are as adaptable as the Tawny Owl, which has proved able to change its woodland hunting techniques designed to catch mammals, and feed in town parks where 93 per cent of its diet consists of birds.

Probably the most vulnerable of owls are those which live on islands where the populations are isolated and probably small. There is often a lack of competition from mainland species and this leads to a trusting approach to human visitors in search of food (not in the case of owls), museum collections or personal trophies.

Many island owls have been reduced almost to extinction by the last two factors.

They have also been used as decoys, using an idea developed by medieval bird catchers. An owl is killed, stuffed and placed in a prominent position to attract small birds intent upon mobbing the predator. The small birds can then be collected for the pot or for museums. Such was the fate of Commerson's Owl (*Otus commersoni*) from Mauritius which, incidentally, was also the home of the Dodo, killed for food. The Soumagnes Owl (*Tyto soumagne*), which inhabited the once-dense forests of Madagascar, became extinct in the 1920s after providing most of Europe's museums with specimens. The same fate, as we have seen, almost befell the Seychelles Owl (*Otus insularis*), which has now been dragged back from the jaws of disaster.

As a final example of this problem, which can be made worse by human introductions of non-indigenous predators, such as cats. Let us look at a New Zealand owl already briefly mentioned on page 78. The White-faced Owl (*Sceloglaux albifacies*) once occurred on both the North and South Islands, also being known as the Laughing Owl from its call, and the Whekau by the Maoris. When the Europeans first came to the Antipodes the owl was common on both islands, but by 1900 the North Island race, *Sceloglaux albifacies rufifacies,* was extinct, while on the South Island *Sceloglaux albifacies albifacies,* the ground-nesting owl, has been greatly reduced through loss of habitat, and more especially by predation of the cats, weasels and stoats introduced from Europe. This owl is now protected by law, although, unfortunately, the predators do not know that. The small population around the region of New Zealand's Southern Alps is bound to be vulnerable and any improvement in status is hardly likely to be dramatic. The lesson is clear — there should never again be any introductions of non-indigenous fauna into the wild places of any country. We tamper with the balance of nature at our peril.

The Future

Finally, we must ask: 'Is there a way forward?' The answer has to be a qualified yes, and if we are careful from now on it might even become an optimistic yes. It can only come, however, through education in classroom, newspaper, on radio and above all on television. Politicians are the only people who can help our threatened birds. If politicians feel that conservation means votes, then they will conserve. We must not cut down trees without replanting. We must not use chemical fertilisers, and herbicides, fungicides and insecticides which we know to be indiscriminate killers. We must study each species of bird in its natural habitat to ascertain its precise requirements and these must then be provided. This applies particularly to rare species which are too often disturbed by muddled-headed ecologists, ambitious photographers and 'keep up with the Joneses' tourists. A rare bird which is shy —and many threatened owls are shy — could well be pushed to extinction by the very people who pretend to love it most. Reserves must be set up and left alone, with an almost total absence of visitors. At the risk of disagreeing with many conservationists, I see more hope for threatened owls in the 1990's than I could in the 1960s. Only time will tell.

Charts

TABLE ONE
GEOLOGICAL TIME AND THE EVOLUTION OF OWLS

ERA	PERIOD		TIME AGO (IN MILLIONS OF YEARS)	
PRECAMBRIAN			2800+	COMMENTS
PALAEOZOIC ERA		*CAMBRIAN*	570	
		ORDOVICIAN	530	
		SILURIAN	440	
		DEVONIAN	410	
		CARBONIFEROUS	345	Flying Insects Evolved
		PERMIAN	280	
MESOZOIC ERA		*TRIASSIC*	225	Flying Reptiles Evolved
		LOWER JURASSIC	195	Birds Evolved
		UPPER JURASSIC	150	
		CRETACEOUS	135	Owls Evolving from Primitive Ancestors during the period
CENOZOIC ERA	TERTIARY PERIOD	*PALAEOCENE*	65	
		EOCENE	54	Strigadae owls recognised
		OLIGOCENE	38	Long Eared owl recognised — the first 'modern owl' to evolve
		MIOCENE	25	Tytonidae owls recognised
		PLIOCENE	7	
	QUATER-NARY PERIOD	*PLEISTOCENE*	2	135 species of owl recognised
		HOLOCENE	1	

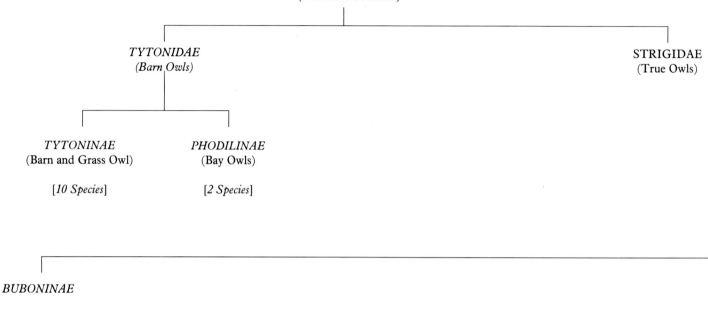

CLASSIFICATION OF OWLS
(STRIGIFORMES)

TYTONIDAE
(Barn Owls)

STRIGIDAE
(True Owls)

TYTONINAE
(Barn and Grass Owl)

[*10 Species*]

PHODILINAE
(Bay Owls)

[*2 Species*]

BUBONINAE

Otus owls	Pyrraglaux	Mimizuku	Lophostrix	Bubo	Pseudoptynx	Ketupa	Scotopelia	Pulsatrix	Nyctea	Surnia
[*37 Species*]	[*1 Species*]	[*1 Species*]	[*1 Species*]	[*11 Species*]	[*1 Species*]	[*4 Species*]	[*3 Species*]	[*3 Species*]	[*1 Species*]	[*1 Specie*

Strix
[*12 Species*]

```
TYTONIDAE                    12 Species
            / BUBONINAE     109 Species
STRIGIDAE <
            \ STRIGINAE      25 Species
                                _____
                    TOTAL    146 Species
                                _____
```

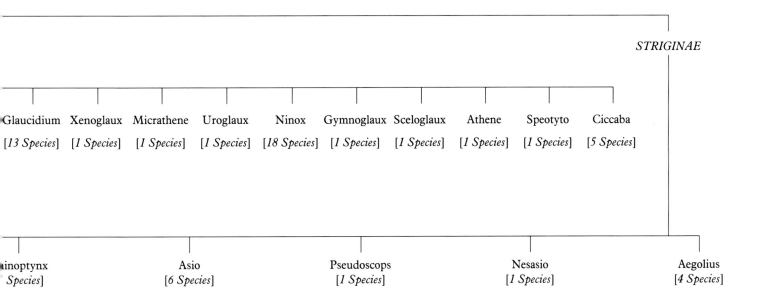

STRIGINAE

Glaucidium Xenoglaux Micrathene Uroglaux Ninox Gymnoglaux Sceloglaux Athene Speotyto Ciccaba

[13 Species] [1 Species] [1 Species] [1 Species] [18 Species] [1 Species] [1 Species] [1 Species] [1 Species] [5 Species]

inoptynx   Asio   Pseudoscops   Nesasio   Aegolius
Species]   [6 Species]   [1 Species]   [1 Species]   [4 Species]

TABLE THREE

A CLASSIFICATION OF THE TYTONIDAE
[BARN OWLS]

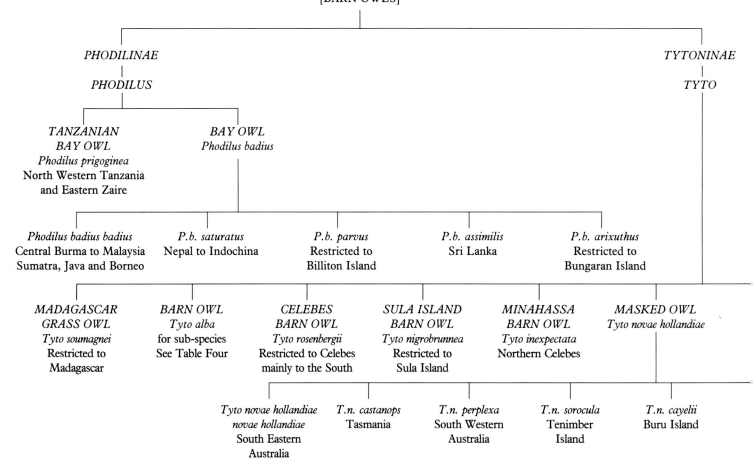

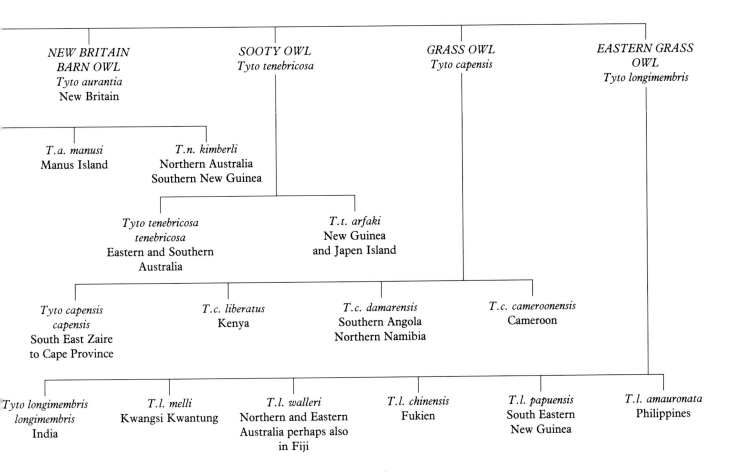

NEW BRITAIN
BARN OWL
Tyto aurantia
New Britain

SOOTY OWL
Tyto tenebricosa

GRASS OWL
Tyto capensis

EASTERN GRASS
OWL
Tyto longimembris

T.a. manusi
Manus Island

T.n. kimberli
Northern Australia
Southern New Guinea

*Tyto tenebricosa
tenebricosa*
Eastern and Southern
Australia

T.t. arfaki
New Guinea
and Japen Island

*Tyto capensis
capensis*
South East Zaire
to Cape Province

T.c. liberatus
Kenya

T.c. damarensis
Southern Angola
Northern Namibia

T.c. cameroonensis
Cameroon

*Tyto longimembris
longimembris*
India

T.l. melli
Kwangsi Kwantung

T.l. walleri
Northern and Eastern
Australia perhaps also
in Fiji

T.l. chinensis
Fukien

T.l. papuensis
South Eastern
New Guinea

T.l. amauronata
Philippines

TABLE FOUR
38 Sub Species of the Barn Owl are
recognised by most authorities
Tyto alba

1	Tyto alba alba Western Europe	14	T.a. deroepstorffi South Andaman Island	26	T.a. bondi Honduras
2	T.a. guttata Central Europe	15	T.a. everetti Sava Islands	27	T.a. lacayana Bahamas
3	T.a. schmitzi Maderia	16	T.a. kuehni Kisar Islands	28	T.a. niveicauda Pinhas Islands
4	T.a gracilirostris Eastern Canaries	17	T.a. sumbaënsis Sumba Islands	29	T.a. furcata Cuba, Jamaica and Cayman Islands
5	T.a. ernesti Corsica and Sardinia	18	T.a. bellonae Bellona Islands	30	T.a. bergei Curaçao Islands
6	T.a. detorta Cape Verde Islands	19	T.a. meeki South Eastern New Guinea	31	T.a. subandeana Columbia, Ecuador
7	T.a. poensis Fernando Po Island	20	T.a. delicatula Australia and the Solomon Islands	32	T.a. contempta Western Columbia, Venezuela and Peru
8	T.a. affinis Gambia, Sudan and Cape Province	21	T.a. crassirostris Boang Island	32	T.a. hellmayri The Guianas and Northern Brazil
9	T.a. thomensis Sao Thomé Island	22	T.a.interposita Santa Cruz, New Hebrides	34	T.a. tuidara Central Brazil, Chile and Argentina
10	T.a. elangeri Arabia, Syria, Iraq	23	T.a. lulu New Caledonia, Fiji, Tonga, Samoa	35	T.a. glaucops Hispaniola and the Tortugas
11	T.a. hypermetra Comoro Island Madagascar	24	T.a. pratincola Central and North East USA and [on to Eastern Nicaragua	36	T.a. nigrescens Dominica
12	T.a. stertens India, Northern Burma, Sri Lanka	25	T.a. guatemalae Western Guatemala to Panama	37	T.a. insularis South Antilles
13	T.a. Javanica Burma, Indochina and Java			38	T.a. punctatissima Galapagos Islands

TABLE FIVE
THE SUB-SPECIES OF THE SPOTTED SCOPS OWL
Otus spilocephalus

1	O.s. spilocephalus Eastern Himalayas to Burma	4	O.s. hambroecki Taiwan	7	O.s. stresemanni Sumatra
2	O.s. huttoni Western Himalayas	5	O.s. siamensis Southern Indo-China and Thailand	8	O.s. luciae Borneo
3	O.s. latouchei South Eastern China and Northern Indo-China	6	O.s. vulpes Malaysia	9	O.s. angelinae Java

These sub-species have been separated on the basis of museum skins, and the taxonomy is in the state of flux.

TABLE SIX

THE SUB-SPECIES OF THE COMMON SCOPS OWL

Otus scops

#		#		#	
1	*Otus scops scops* Western Europe, Russia and Central Africa	8	*O.s. modestus* Southern China, Indo-China	15	*O.s. botelensis* Botel and Tobago Islands
2	*O.s. cyprius* Cyprus	9	*O.s. malayanus* Malaysia	16	*O.s. calayensis* Calayan Islands
3	*O.s. cycladum* Crete and the Cyclades	10	*O.s. sunia* Himalayas and Northern India	17	*O.s. longicornis* Luzon Island
4	*O.s. turanicus* Northern Iran and Transcaspia	11	*O.s. rufipennis* Central and Southern India	18	*O.s. rumblonis* Romblon and Banton Islands
5	*O.s. pulchellus* Caucasus and Russia into Central Asia and North West India	12	*O.s. leggei* Sri Lanka	19	*O.s. mantananensis* Mantanani Island
6	*O.s. stictonotus* Manchuria China Taiwan	13	*O.s. interpositus* Borodina Island	20	*O.s. cuyenensis* Cuto Island
7	*O.s. japonicus* Northern Japan	14	*O.s. elegans* Riukiu Island The Status of this sub-species is subject to some debate	21	*O.s. mindorensis* Mindoro Island

TABLE SEVEN

THE SUB-SPECIES OF THE
AFRICAN SCOPS OWL

Otus senegalensis

1	*Otus senegalensis senegalensis* [Senegal to Central Sudan]	5	*O.s. socotranus* Island of Socotra	9	*O.s. hendersonii* Anlola and South Western Zaire
2	*O.s. pygmea* Southern Sudan and North Western Ethiopia	6	*O.s. ugandae* North and North Eastern Zaire and Western Uganda	10	*O.s. pusillus* Mozambique, Eastern Malawi and Eastern Zimbabwe
3	*O.s. caecus* Central and Southern Ethiopia, Somalia and Northern Kenya	7	*O.s. graueri* Eastern Kenya and Tanzania	11	*O.s. intermedius* Namibia to Southern Mozambique and Northern Natal
4	*O.s. pamelae* Saudi Arabia	8	*O.s. feae* Annobon Island	12	*O.s. latipennis* Cape Province in South Africa

TABLE EIGHT

THE SUB-SPECIES OF THE
CELEBES SCOPS OWL (also called the Indonesian Scops Owls)

Otus manadensis

1	*Otus manadensis manadensis* The Celebes	5	*O.m. mendeni* Peling Islands	10	*O.m. albiventris* Islands of Lomblen, Lombok Sumbawa and Flores
2	*O.m. steerei* Tumindao Islands	6	*sulaensis* goli Islands	11	*O.m. tempestatis* Island of Wetar
3	*O.m. sibutuensis* Sibutu Islands	7	*O.m. kalidupae* Island of Kalidupa	12	*O.m. morotensis* Ternate and Morotai Islands
4	*O.s. siaoënsis* Siao Islands	8	*O.m. leucospilus* Batjan and Halmahera Islands	13	*O.m. bouruensis* Barn Islands
		9	*O.m. magicus* Ceram and Ambon Islands		

114

TABLE NINE

*THE DIVISION OF THE COLLARED SCUP OWL
INTO 23 ISLAND SUB SPECIES MANY
SEPARATED BY LARGE EXPANSES IF SEA*

Otus bakkamoena

#		#		#	
1	*Otus bakkamoena bakkomoena* Southern India and Sri Lanka	9	*O.b. glabripes* Taiwan	16	*O.b. kangeana* Kangean Islands
2	*O.b. marathae* Central India	10	*O.b. erythrocampe* Southern China Northern Vietnam	17	*O.b. cnephaeus* Malaysia
3	*O.b. gangeticus* North West and North Central India	11	*O.b. aurorae* Northern China	18	*O.b. hypnodes* Sumatra and Singapore
4	*O.b. deserticolor* South East Saudi Arabia, Pakistan Southern Iran	12	*O.b. pryeri* Islands of Okinawa and Hachija	19	*O.b. lempiji* Java, Bali and Borneo
5	*O.b. plumipes* North West Himalayas	13	*O.b. semitorques* Japan and Kurile Island	20	*O.b. mentawi* Pagi, Sipora and Siberut Islands
6	*O.b. manipurensis* Manipur, Assam	14	*O.b. ussuriensis* Southern Manchuria to Korea	21	*O.b. fuliginosus* Palawan Island
7	*O.b. lettia* Eastern Himalayas as far as Burma and Northern Thailand	15	*O.b. condorensis* Pulo Condor Island	22	*O.b. everetti* Basilan Samar and Mindanao
8	*O.b. umbratilis* Hainan Islands			23	*O.b. boholensis* Bohol Islands

TABLE TEN

THE SUB-SPECIES OF THE SCREECH OWL

Otus asio

1	*Otus asio asio* Eastern Virginia to Kansas	9	*O.a. swenki* Central and Southern Canada down to Oklahoma	16	*O.a. cardonensis* California and Western Baja
2	*O.a. kennicotti* South Eastern Alaska to the West of Washington	10	*O.a. maevius* Central and Eastern Canada to Georgia	17	*O.a. yumanensis* South Western Arizona
3	*O.a. brewsteri* Southern Washington to North West California	11	*O.a. floridanus* The Gulf Coast and Florida	18	*O.a. clazus* Southern California
4	*O.a. bendirei* Western California	12	*O.a. hasbroucki* Central Oklahoma to Northern Texas	19	*O.a. quercinus* South Western California
5	*O.a. macfarlanei* Southern British Columbia as far as Idaho	13	*O.a. mychophilus* North and Central Utah to Northern Arizona	20	*O.a. xantusi* California and South Baja
6	*O.a. inyoensis* Eastern California to Northern Utah	14	*O.a. mccallii* Southern Texas and North Eastern Mexico	21	*O.a. vinaceus* North East Sinaloa
7	*O.a. maxwelliae* Eastern Montana to Central Colorado	15	*O.a. cineraceous* Central Arizona to North West Texas	22	*O.a. sinaloesis* South East Sonora and North West Sinaloa
8	*O.a. aitkeni* Central Colorado to Northern Mexico				

TABLE ELEVEN

THE SUB-SPECIES OF THE SPOTTED OR WHISKERED
SCREECH OWL

Otus trichopsis

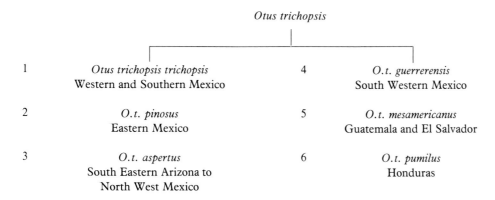

1	*Otus trichopsis trichopsis* Western and Southern Mexico	4	*O.t. guerrerensis* South Western Mexico
2	*O.t. pinosus* Eastern Mexico	5	*O.t. mesamericanus* Guatemala and El Salvador
3	*O.t. aspertus* South Eastern Arizona to North West Mexico	6	*O.t. pumilus* Honduras

TABLE TWELVE

THE SUB-SPECIES OF THE VERMICULATED
SCREECH OWL

Otus guatemalae

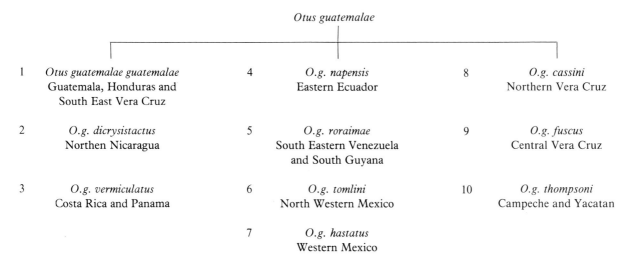

1	*Otus guatemalae guatemalae* Guatemala, Honduras and South East Vera Cruz	4	*O.g. napensis* Eastern Ecuador	8	*O.g. cassini* Northern Vera Cruz
2	*O.g. dicrysistactus* Northen Nicaragua	5	*O.g. roraimae* South Eastern Venezuela and South Guyana	9	*O.g. fuscus* Central Vera Cruz
3	*O.g. vermiculatus* Costa Rica and Panama	6	*O.g. tomlini* North Western Mexico	10	*O.g. thompsoni* Campeche and Yacatan
		7	*O.g. hastatus* Western Mexico		

TABLE THIRTEEN

THE SUB-SPECIES OF THE TROPICAL
OR CHOLIBA SCREECH OWL

Otus choliba

1	*Otus choliba choliba* Southern Brazil, Paraguay, Northern Argentina and Uraguay		5	*O.c. crucigerus* Central Brazil and the upper [Amazon
2	*O.c. wetmorei* Southern Eastern Bolivia, West Paraguay and North Western Argentina		6	*O.c. alticola* Central Colombia
3	*O.c. luctisonus* Costa Rica to North West Colombia		7	*O.c. decussatus* South Central and Eastern [Brazil
4	*O.c. margaritae* Northern Columbia, Northern Venezuela and the Island of Margarita		8	*O.c. duidae* South Eastern Venezuela

TABLE FOURTEEN

THE SUB SPECIES OF THE GREAT HORNED OWL

Bubo virginianus

1   *Bubo virginianus virginianus*
     [South Eastern Canada, and
     [the Eastern and Central States of
     [the United States

2   *B.v. heterocnemis*
     [Eastern Canada

3   *B.v. pallescens*
     [South Western United States and
     [North and Central Mexico

4   *B.v. occidentalis*
     [West Central Canada as far
     [as Western Central USA

5   *B.v. wapacuthu*
     [West and Central Canada

6   *B.v. pacificus*
     [South Oregon and California

7   *B.v.elachistus*
     [California and
     [Southern Baja

8   *B.v. mayensis*
     [Central Mexico to
     [Western Panama

9   *B.v. elutus*
     [Eastern Colombia

10   *B.v. columbianus*
     [Central Columbia

11   *B.v. nigrescens*
     [Western Ecuador

12   *B.v. scotinus*
     [Eastern Venezuela

13   *B.v. deserti*
     [Eastern Brazil

14   *B.v. nacurutu*
     [Peru and North Western Brazil
     [as far as Tierra del Fuego

15   *B.v. saturatus*
     [South Western Alaska to
     [California]

16   *B.v. iagophonus*
     [Central Alaska to North East
     [Oregon and Idaho

17   *B.v. algistus*
     [Western Alaska

TABLE FIFTEEN

THE SUB-SPECIES OF THE EAGLE OWL

Bubo bubo

1 *Bubo bubo bubo* Scandinavia, Western Europe as far as Western USSR	9 *B.b. ussuriensis* Lower Amur, Ussuriland	16 *B.b. tibetanus* Central Tibet and North West China
2 *B.b. hispanus* Iberia	10 *B.b. inexpectatus* Manchuria and Northern China	17 *B.b. kiautschensis* Central and Eastern China
3 *B.b. interpositus* South Western Russia to Syria	11 *B.b tenuipes* Korea, Hokkaido and South Kurile Islands	18 *B.b. jarlandi* South East Yunnan
4 *B.b. ruthenus* South East Russia	12 *B.b. borissowi* Sakhalin	19 *B.b. swinhoei* South Eastern China
5 *B.b. sibiricus* Western and Central Asia	13 *B.b. turcomanus* Turkestan	20 *B.b. hemachalana* Western Tien Shan and Western Himalayas
6 *B.b. yenisseensis* Central and East Central Siberia	14 *B.b. zaissanensis* South and Central Asia	21 *B.b. bengalensis* North and Central India
7 *B.b. dauricus* Northern Mongolia	15 *B.b. nikolskii* Iran and Iraq	22 *B.b. ascalaphus* North African scrub fringing [the desert
8 *B.b jakutensis* North Eastern Siberia		23 *B.b. desertorum* North African desert

TABLE SIXTEEN

THE SUB-SPECIES OF THE LEAST PYGMY OWL

Glaucidium minutissimum

1	*Glaucidium minutissimum minutissimum* Guyana Surinam and Brazil	5	*G.m. oberholseri* Central and Southern Sinalua
2	*G.m. rarum* Costa Rica and Panama	6	*G.m. griscomi* North Eastern Guerrero and South Western Morelus
3	*G.m. griseiceps* Eastern Guatemala, Belize and Eastern Honduras	7	*G.m. occultum* East Oaxaca and Chiapas
4	*G.m. palmarum* Western Mexico	8	*G.m. sanchezi* San Luis Potosi

TABLE SEVENTEEN

SUB SPECIES OF THE FERRUGINOUS PYGMY OWL

Glaucidium brasilianum

1	*Glaucidium brasilianum brasilianum* West and South Amazon area and North East Argentina	5	*G.b. ucayalae* South East Columbia as far as Peru	9	*G.b. phaloenoides* North Venezuela and Trinidad
2	*G.b. pallens* East Bolivia, Western Paraguay, North Western Argentina	6	*G.b. duidae* Found on Mount Duida in Venezuela	10	*G.b. medianum* North Columbia
3	*G.b. tocumanum* Western Argentina	7	*G.b. margaritae* Margarita Island	11	*G.b. ridgwayi* Southern Texas to Central Panama
4	*G.b. nanum* Southern Chile and Southern Argentina	8	*G.b. olivaceum* Another mountain species from Venezuela found on Mount Augun-tepui	12	*G.b. cactorum* Southern Arizona and Western Mexico

121

TABLE EIGHTEEN

THE SUB-SPECIES OF THE CUCKOO OWL

Glaucidium cuculoides

1	*Glaucidium cuculoides cuculoides* Western Himalayas	6	*G.c. delacouri* Northern Indo-China
2	*G.c. castanonotum* Sri Lanka	7	*G.c. deignani* South East Thailand and Southern Indo-China
3	*G.c. rufescens* North East India and North Burma	8	*G.c. whitelyi* West, Central and South East China and North East Vietnam
4	*G.c. brugeli* Southern Burma and Southern Thailand	9	*G.c. persimile* Hainan Island
5	*G.c. austerum* North Eastern Assam	10	*G.c. castanopterum* Java and Bali

TABLE NINETEEN

THE SUB-SPECIES OF THE BARKING OR WINKING OWL

Ninox connivens

1	*Ninox connivens connivens* South and Eastern Australia	5	*N.c. occidentalis* North Western Australia and Northern Territory
2	*N.c. addenda* South Western Australia	6	*N.c. assimilis* Eastern New Guinea, Vulcan and Dampier Island
3	*N.c. enigma* Central and North Queensland	7	*N.c. rufostrigata* North Moluccas
4	*N.c. peninsularis* Cape York Peninsula		

TABLE TWENTY

THE SUB-SPECIES OF THE BOOBOOK
OR MOREPOKE OWL

Ninox novaeseelandiae

1	*Ninox novaeseelandliae novaeseelandiae* South Island, New Zealand	6	*N.n. boobook* Eastern Australia	11	*N.n. remigialis* Kei Island
2	*N.n. venatia* North Island New Zealand	7	*N.n. marmorata* South and South West Australia	12	*N.n. fusca* Timor Island
3	*N.n. undulata* Norfolk Island	8	*N.n. lurida* North East Queensland	13	*N.n. plesseni* Alor Island
4	*N.n. albaria* Lord Howe Island	9	*N.n. ocellata* NorthernAustralia and Melville Island	14	*N.n. cinnamomina* Barbar Island
5	*N.n. leucopsis* Tasmania	10	*N.n. pusilla* Southern New Guinea	15	*N.n. rudolfi* Sumba Island

TABLE TWENTY ONE

THE SUB-SPECIES OF THE BROWN HAWK OWL

Ninox scutulata

1	*Ninox scutulata scutulata* Japan, East China to lesser Sunda Island	6	*N.s. obscura* Andaman and Nicobar Islands
2	*N.s. ussuriensis* North East Asia	7	*N.s. malaccensis* Southern Malaysia, Sumatra and Bangka Island
3	*N.s. burmanica* Southern Assam to Malaysia and Indo-China	8	*N.s. javanensis* Western Java
4	*N.s. lugubris* North and Central India	9	*N.s. borneensis* Borneo and the Northern Natuna Island
5	*N.s. hirsuta* Southern India and Sri Lanka	10	*N.s. randi* The Philippines

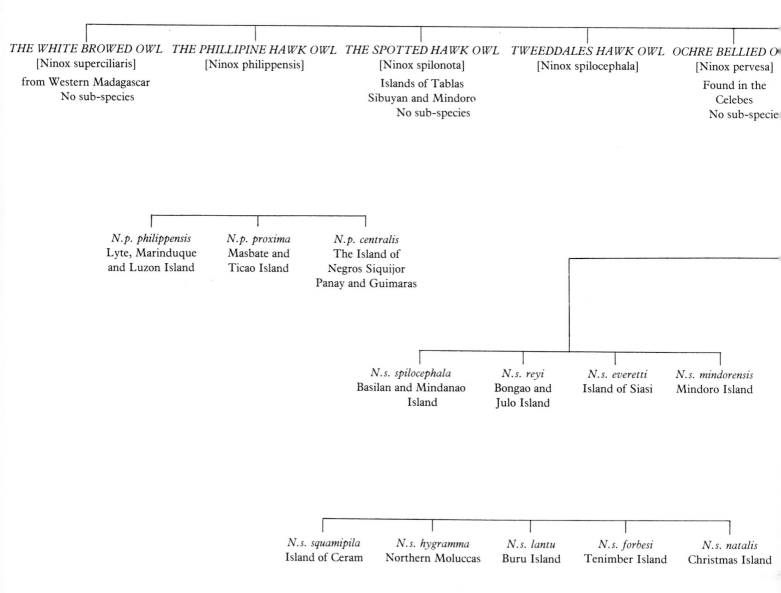

THE WHITE BROWED OWL
[Ninox superciliaris]
from Western Madagascar
No sub-species

THE PHILLIPINE HAWK OWL
[Ninox philippensis]

THE SPOTTED HAWK OWL
[Ninox spilonota]
Islands of Tablas
Sibuyan and Mindoro
No sub-species

TWEEDDALES HAWK OWL
[Ninox spilocephala]

OCHRE BELLIED O
[Ninox pervesa]
Found in the
Celebes
No sub-specie

N.p. philippensis
Lyte, Marinduque
and Luzon Island

N.p. proxima
Masbate and
Ticao Island

N.p. centralis
The Island of
Negros Siquijor
Panay and Guimaras

N.s. spilocephala
Basilan and Mindanao
Island

N.s. reyi
Bongao and
Julo Island

N.s. everetti
Island of Siasi

N.s. mindorensis
Mindoro Island

N.s. squamipila
Island of Ceram

N.s. hygramma
Northern Moluccas

N.s. lantu
Buru Island

N.s. forbesi
Tenimber Island

N.s. natalis
Christmas Island

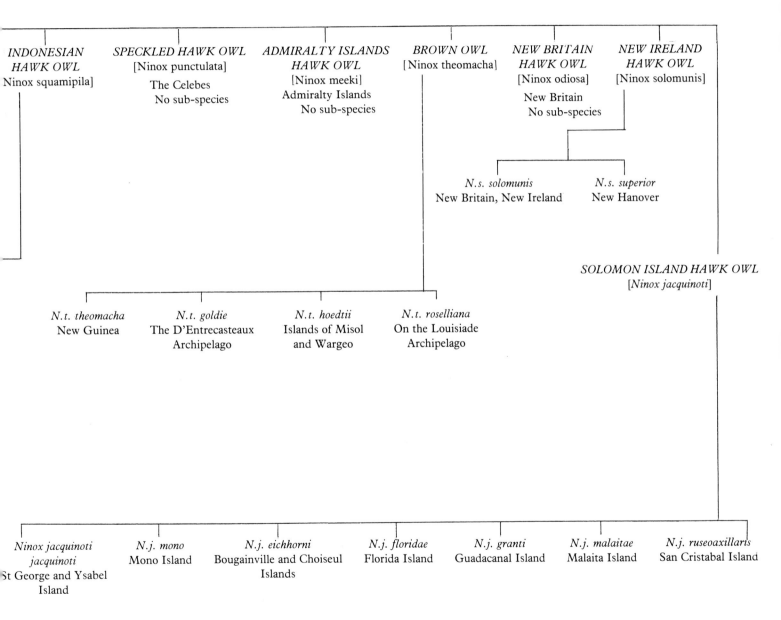

INDONESIAN
HAWK OWL
Ninox squamipila]

SPECKLED HAWK OWL
[Ninox punctulata]
The Celebes
No sub-species

ADMIRALTY ISLANDS
HAWK OWL
[Ninox meeki]
Admiralty Islands
No sub-species

BROWN OWL
[Ninox theomacha]

NEW BRITAIN
HAWK OWL
[Ninox odiosa]
New Britain
No sub-species

NEW IRELAND
HAWK OWL
[Ninox solomunis]

N.s. solomunis
New Britain, New Ireland

N.s. superior
New Hanover

SOLOMON ISLAND HAWK OWL
[Ninox jacquinoti]

N.t. theomacha
New Guinea

N.t. goldie
The D'Entrecasteaux
Archipelago

N.t. hoedtii
Islands of Misol
and Wargeo

N.t. roselliana
On the Louisiade
Archipelago

Ninox jacquinoti
jacquinoti
St George and Ysabel
Island

N.j. mono
Mono Island

N.j. eichhorni
Bougainville and Choiseul
Islands

N.j. floridae
Florida Island

N.j. granti
Guadacanal Island

N.j. malaitae
Malaita Island

N.j. ruseoaxillaris
San Cristabal Island

TABLE TWENTY THREE

THE SUB-SPECIES OF
THE LITTLE OWL

Athene noctua

1 *Athene noctua noctua* Central Europe	6 *A.n. saharae* Southern Morocco to Northern Saudi Arabia	11 *A.n. ludlowi* Tibet
2 *A.n. vidalii* Western Europe	7 *A.n. solitudinis* Central Sahara	12 *A.n. impasta* Kokonor, Western Kansu
3 *A.n. sarda* Sardinia	8 *A.n. lilith* Syria and Israel	13 *A.n. plumipes* East Central Asia
4 *A.n. indigena* Northern Iran, Greece and Southern Russia	9 *A.n. bactriana* Transcaspia as far Pakistan	14 *A.n. spilogastra* Eastern Sudan, North Eastern Ethiopia
5 *A.n. glaux* North Africa	10 *A.n. orientalis* North East Russia and China	15 *A.n. somaliensis* Somalia and Eastern Ethiopia

TABLE TWENTY FOUR

THE SUB-SPECIES OF THE BURROWING OWL

Athena cunicularia

1	*Athena cunicularia cunicularia* Southern Bolivia, and from the South of Brazil to Tierra del Fuego	7	*A.c. apurensis* North and Central Venezuela	14	*A.c. brackyptera* Northern Venezuela and the Island of Margarita
2	*A.c. partridgei* Argentina and the Corrientes	8	*A.c. intermedia* Western Peru	1	*A.c. arubensis* Island of Aruba
3	*A.c. glallaria* East and Southern Brazil	9	*A.c. punensis* South West of Ecuador and North Western Peru	16	*A.c. troglodytes* Island of Gonave and Hispaniola considering trogodytes means a cave dweller this is the best named of all the sub-species
4	*A.c. nanodes* South Western Peru	10	*A.c. pichinchae* Western Ecuador	17	*A.c. floridana* Central and Southern Florida and the Bahama Islands
5	*A.c. boliviana* Bolivia	11	*A.c. tolimae* Western Columbia	18	*A.c. rostrata* Clarion Islands
6	*A.c. juninensis* Central Peru and the extreme West of Bolivia	12	*A.c. carrikeri* Eastern Columbia	19	*A.c. hypugaea* Found from South Western Canada through the United States to Western Mexico and is therefore the most thoroughly studied of all the sub- species
		13	*A.c. minor* Southern Guyana, North Eastern Brazil and to the South of Surinam		

TABLE TWENTY FIVE

THE SUB-SPECIES OF THE MOTTLED OWL

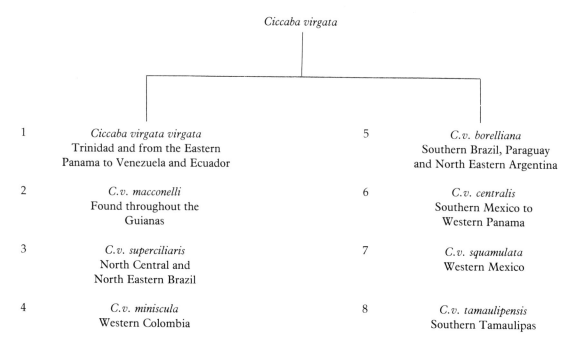

Ciccaba virgata

1   *Ciccaba virgata virgata*
Trinidad and from the Eastern
Panama to Venezuela and Ecuador

5   *C.v. borelliana*
Southern Brazil, Paraguay
and North Eastern Argentina

2   *C.v. macconelli*
Found throughout the
Guianas

6   *C.v. centralis*
Southern Mexico to
Western Panama

3   *C.v. superciliaris*
North Central and
North Eastern Brazil

7   *C.v. squamulata*
Western Mexico

4   *C.v. miniscula*
Western Colombia

8   *C.v. tamaulipensis*
Southern Tamaulipas

TABLE TWENTY SIX

THE SUB-SPECIES OF THE BROWN WOOD OWL

Strix leptogrammica

1	*Strix leptogrammica leptogrammica* South and Central Borneo	6	*S.l. nyctiphasma* Island of Banjak	11	*S.l. maingayi* Southern Burma, Malaysia and Southern Thailand
2	*S.l. vaga* Northern Borneo	7	*S.l. myrtha* Sumatra	12	*S.l. ochrogenys* Sri Lanka
3	*S.l. bartelsi* West and Central Java	8	*S.l. caligata* Taiwan and the Island of Hainan	13	*S.l. connectens* Central India
4	*S.l. chaseni* The Island of Billiton	9	*S.l. inotiana* Southern Indo-China	14	*S.l. indranee* Southern India
5	*S.l. niasensis* The Island of Nias	10	*S.l. ticehursti* South East China and Northern Indo-China	15	*S.l. newarensis* Himalayas through Northern Burma and Northern Thailand

TABLE TWENTY SEVEN

THE SUB-SPECIES OF THE TAWNY OWL

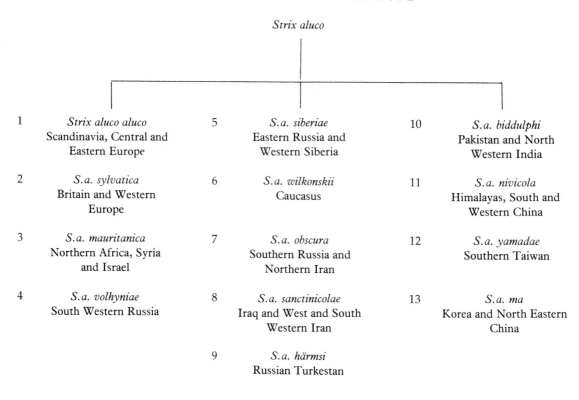

1   *Strix aluco aluco*
Scandinavia, Central and
Eastern Europe

2   *S.a. sylvatica*
Britain and Western
Europe

3   *S.a. mauritanica*
Northern Africa, Syria
and Israel

4   *S.a. volhyniae*
South Western Russia

5   *S.a. siberiae*
Eastern Russia and
Western Siberia

6   *S.a. wilkonskii*
Caucasus

7   *S.a. obscura*
Southern Russia and
Northern Iran

8   *S.a. sanctinicolae*
Iraq and West and South
Western Iran

9   *S.a. härmsi*
Russian Turkestan

10   *S.a. biddulphi*
Pakistan and North
Western India

11   *S.a. nivicola*
Himalayas, South and
Western China

12   *S.a. yamadae*
Southern Taiwan

13   *S.a. ma*
Korea and North Eastern
China

TABLE TWENTY EIGHT

THE SUB-SPECIES OF THE URAL OWL

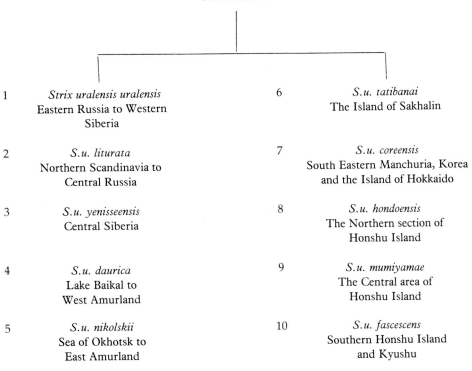

Strix urelensis

1	*Strix uralensis uralensis* Eastern Russia to Western Siberia	6	*S.u. tatibanai* The Island of Sakhalin
2	*S.u. liturata* Northern Scandinavia to Central Russia	7	*S.u. coreensis* South Eastern Manchuria, Korea and the Island of Hokkaido
3	*S.u. yenisseensis* Central Siberia	8	*S.u. hondoensis* The Northern section of Honshu Island
4	*S.u. daurica* Lake Baikal to West Amurland	9	*S.u. mumiyamae* The Central area of Honshu Island
5	*S.u. nikolskii* Sea of Okhotsk to East Amurland	10	*S.u. fascescens* Southern Honshu Island and Kyushu

TABLE TWENTY NINE

THE SUB-SPECIES OF THE SHORT-EARED OWL

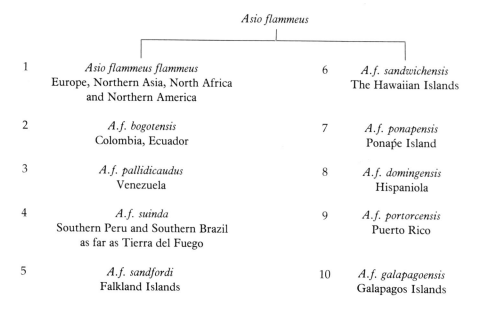

Asio flammeus

1	*Asio flammeus flammeus* Europe, Northern Asia, North Africa and Northern America	6	*A.f. sandwichensis* The Hawaiian Islands
2	*A.f. bogotensis* Colombia, Ecuador	7	*A.f. ponapensis* Ponape Island
3	*A.f. pallidicaudus* Venezuela	8	*A.f. domingensis* Hispaniola
4	*A.f. suinda* Southern Peru and Southern Brazil as far as Tierra del Fuego	9	*A.f. portorcensis* Puerto Rico
5	*A.f. sandfordi* Falkland Islands	10	*A.f. galapagoensis* Galapagos Islands

TABLE THIRTY

THE SUB-SPECIES OF TENGMALM'S OWL

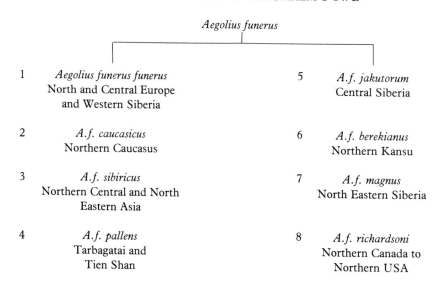

Aegolius funerus

1	*Aegolius funerus funerus* North and Central Europe and Western Siberia	5	*A.f. jakutorum* Central Siberia
2	*A.f. caucasicus* Northern Caucasus	6	*A.f. berekianus* Northern Kansu
3	*A.f. sibiricus* Northern Central and North Eastern Asia	7	*A.f. magnus* North Eastern Siberia
4	*A.f. pallens* Tarbagatai and Tien Shan	8	*A.f. richardsoni* Northern Canada to Northern USA

SELECTED BIBLIOGRAPHY

Angell, T. 1974. *Owls*. University of Washington Press, Seattle

Benson, C.W. 1981. Ecological differences between the Grass Owl *Tyto capensis* and the Marsh Owl *Asio capensis*. *Bull, Brit, Orn. Club*. 101 (4) 372-6

Beven, G. 1964. The food of tawny owls in London. *London Bird Report* 29: 56-72

Bezzel, E. et al. 1976. On the diet of the eagle owl *Bubo bubo*. *J. Orn Lpz* 117: 210-38

Boddam-Whetham, A.D. 1969. Behaviour of young Grass Owls. *African Wild Life* 23: 70-2

Brdicka, I. 1970. 'Eurasian eagle Owl' in J. Gooders (ed), *Birds of the world*. (IPC London) 4: 1314-16

Brock, J. 1970. 'Eurasian pygmy Owl' in J. Gooders (ed), *Birds of the world*. (IPC London) 4: 1329-30

Brock, J. 1970. 'Tengmalm's Owl' in J. Gooders (ed), *Birds of the world*. (IPC London) 5: 1365-7

Brooke, R.K., Oatley, T.B., Hurley, M.E. & Kurtz, D.W. 1983. The South African distribution and status of the nominate race of the Barred Owl. *Ostrich* 54: 173-4

Brown, L. 1970. *African Birds of Prey*. London: Collins

Brown, L. 1976. *Birds of Prey: Their Biology and Ecology*. Feltham: Hamlyn

Brown, L. 1979. *Encounters with Nature*. Oxford: Oxford University Press

Brown, L.H. 1976. Observations on Pel's Fishing Owl. *Scotopelia peli*. *Bull. Brit. Orn. Club* 96: 49-53

Bruno, U. 1973. Observations on the biology of the little owl *Athena noctua*. *Anz. Orn. Ges. Bayern* 12: 163-75

Buckley, J. 1976. Barn Owl *Tyto alba alba* pellets from Portugal . *Bol. Soc. Port. Clienc. Nat* 16: 133-6

Bunn, D.S., Warburton, A.B. & Wilson, R.D.S. 1982. *The Barn Owl*. Calton T. & A.D. Poyser

Burton, J.A. 1970. 'Little Owl' in J. Gooders (ed), *Birds of the world*. (IPC London) 4: 1336-9

Burton, J.A. (ed) 1973, *Owls of the World*, Weert: Peter Lowe

Clark, R.J., Smith, D.G. & Delso, L.H. 1978. *Working Bibliography of Owls of the World*. Washington: National Wildlife Federation

De Bruijn, O. 1970. Feeding ecology of the barn owl, *Tyto alba*, in the Netherlands. *Limosa* 52: 91-154

Eckert, A.W. 1974. *The Owls of North America*. Doubleday & Co Garden City, N.Y.

Everett, M. 1977. Natural history of owls. Hamlyn, London

Everett, M. and Sharrock, J.T.R. 1980. The European Atlas; Owls. Br. *Birds* 73: 239-56

Ferguson-Lees, I.J. 1970. 'Eurasian scops owl' in J. Gooders (ed), *Birds of the world*. (IPC London) 4: 1303-6

Ferguson-Lees, I.J. 1970. 'Ural Owl' in J. Gooders (ed), *Birds of the world*. (IPC London) 5: 1347-9

Ferguson-Lees, I.J. 1970. 'Great grey Owl' in J. Gooders (ed), *Birds of the world*. (IPC London) 5: 1352-7

Gargett, V. 1976. Dead or alive? *African Wildlife* 30: 40-1

Glue, D.E. 1970. 'Owl pellets' in J. Gooders (ed), *Birds of the world*. (IPC London) 5: 1368-70

Glue, D.E. 1977. Breeding biology of long-eared owls. *Br. Birds* 70: 318-31

Grossman, M.L. and Hamlet, J. 1965. *Birds of Prey of the World*. Cassell & Co. London

Harrison, J. 1970. 'Snowy Owl' in J. Goodes (ed), *Birds of the world.* (IPC London) 4: 1322-6

Hibbert-Ware, A. 1937. Report of the little owl food enquiry 1936-7. *BR. Birds* 31: 162-264

Holmberg, T. 1976. Variation in prey selection by the tawny owl (Strix aluco). *Flora Fauna (Stockh.)* 71: 97-107

Hosking, E.J. & Newberry, C.W. 1945, *Birds of the Night.* London: Collins

Hosking, E. & Flegg, J. 1982. *Eric Hosking's Owls.* London: Pelham Books.

Johansen, H. 1978. Nest site selection by the Ural Owl. *Flora Fauna (Stockh.)* 73: 207-10

Liversedge, T.N. 1980. A study of Pel's Fishing Owl *Scotopelia peli* Bonaparte 1850 in the 'Pan Handle' region of the Okavango Delta, Botswana. *Proceedings 4th Pan-African Ornithological Congress* 291-9

Martin, J. 1956. Nest of South African Wood Owl. *Ostrich* 27: 149-50

McLachlan, G.R. & Liversidge R. 1978. *Roberts Birds of South Africa.* Cape Town: Jon Voelcker Bird Book Fund

Mead, C. 1970. 'Short-eared Owl' in J. Gooders (ed), *Birds of the world.* (IPC London) 5: 1362-5

Mikkola, H. 1976. Owls killing and killed by other raptors in Europe. *BR. Birds* 69: 144-54

Mikkola, H. 1983. *Owls of Europe,* Calton: T & A.D. Poyser.

Muir, R.C. 1954. Calling and feeding rates of fledged tawny owls. *Bird Study,* 1, 111-17

Mysterud, I. & Dunker, H. 1979. Mammal ear mimicry: a hypothesis on the behavioural function of owl 'horns'. *Animal Behaviour* 27: 315-16

Nilsson, I.N. 1977. Hunting methods and habitat utilization of two tawny owls (Strix aluco L.). *Fauna Flora (Stockh.)* 72: 156-63

Parslow, J. 1970. 'Hawk Owl' in J. Gooder (ed), *Birds of the world* (IPC London) 4: 1327-9

Payne, R.S. 1962. How the barn owl locates its prey by hearing. *Living Bird* 1, 15-89

Prestt, I. 1970. 'Barn Owl' in J. Gooders (ed), *Birds of the world.* (IPC London) 4: 1295-1300

Scherzinger, W. 1974. Study on the ecology of the pygmy owl *Glaucidium passerinum* in the Bayerischer Wald National Park. *Anz. Orn. Ges Bayern* 13: 121-56

Schmidt, E. 1973. The food of the Barn Owl *(Tyto Alba)* in Europe *Z. agnew. Zool.* 60: 43-70

Scott, J. 1980. Further notes on the Wood Owl. *Honeyguide* 103/104: 4-8

Sparks, J. & Soper, T. 1970. *Owls: Their Natural and Unnatural History.* Newton Abbot. L. David and Charles

Steyn, P. 1979. Observations on Pearl-spotted and Barred Owls. *Bokmakierie* 31: 50-60

Steyn, P. 1982. *Birds of Prey of Southern Africa.* Cape Town: David Philip

Steyn, P. 1984. *A Delight of Owls.* Cape Town: David Philip

Steyn, P. & Scott, J. 1973. Notes on the breeding biology of the Wood Owl. *Ostrich* 44: 118-25

Steyn, P. & Tredgold, D. 1977. Observations on the Cape Eagle Owl. *Bokmakierie* 29: 31-42

Steyn, P. & Myburgh, N. 1983. Prey of the Cape Eagle Owl at Brandvlei, Cape. *African Wildlife* 37: 127

Ticehurst, C.B. 1935. On the food of the Barn Owl and bearing on Barn Owl populations. *Ibis* 2: 329:35

Tyler, H. and Phullips, D. 1977. *Owls by Day and Night.* Naturegraph Books: 987 Happy Camp California

Vernon, C.J. 1972. An analysis of owl pellets collected in Southern Africa. *Ostrich* 43: 109-24

Weaving, A.J.S. 1970. Observations on the breeding behaviour of the Scops Owl. *Bokmakierie* 22: 58-61

Wilson, V.J. 1970. Notes on the breeding and feeding habits of a pair of Barn Owls, *Tyto alba* (Scopoli), in Rhodesia. Arnoldia (Rhodesia) 4 (34) 1.8